THE ENGLISH AT LOVE

THE ENGLISH AT LOVE

Gerald McKnight

A FOUR SQUARE BOOK

Although the incidents described in this book are for the most part factual, in that they happened more or less as described, they did not happen to the people I have named nor to anyone of a similar name. Where a place-name or any mark of identification is included, this has been invented to avoid all possible embarrassment to the actual individuals concerned.

The English, or so I am told, do not look upon women with quite the same reverence as we Continentals. Women in England seem to be an excuse, rather than a reason.

Gunther Sachs, husband
of Brigitte Bardot

INTRODUCTION

What the British must never believe about themselves is that they are good at games, strong in adversity, but lousy in bed. It is a myth invented by jealous foreigners. Other nationals may be exposed as wife-beaters, woman-haters and worse without making a ha'p'orth of difference to this silly legend. But of course the British encourage it.

Why? There are scores of reasons, but only one that makes any sense. Deep down inside their fast-beating hearts, every British male and his mate resent the passing of the curtained four-poster. Without spiritual secrecy and physical privacy, they feel painfully naked.

That is why they laugh themselves hoarse at broad, lavatory jokes, yet telephone a shocked chorus of objection if anyone uses a four-letter word in all seriousness before a television camera.

As that master of genteel smut, Mr Philip Godfrey, used to tell us from the stage of the Players Theatre: "There must be a *modicum* of filth, but let's get it out of the way as quickly as possible."

It is the British way, as it is the British way to encourage a shockingly high incidence of criminal sexual violence in a society driven to the limits of frustration by repressive laws.

Plainly, this is not the only group of countries where a man and a woman may live together, sleep together and breed a family together without ever seeing each other naked. But it may well be the only one boasting, at the same time, that it is "emancipated" and "enlightened".

It is also, quite certainly, the sole segment of the human race which indulges in public ridicule of its male virility.

In the twenties, the British man was delighted to be caricatured as far too bored to be adequate as a lover of anything but horses, hunting and house-parties. The thirties produced an equally well-received mockery of the British lover, as a stammering, immature creature, dazzled by "flappers", night-club hostesses and all alluring foreign ladies. During the war, poor pay and rough uniforms combined to make mincemeat of these islands' defenders in the international seduction stakes, whenever the

7

competition appeared flashing dollar bills and hotel reservations. Once again, this was unprotestingly accepted.

And since? Well, the myth has continued to grow in all corners of the world, particularly those where the "white officer with black privates" has been forced to step down from his ceremonial grandstand. It is a curious irony that nothing has done more to convince the world of our feebleness as lovers than the loving care with which we have released our empire, discharged our debts and chivalrously played our role of St George during this century.

It is the age, we are told, of the common man. But of the uncommon lover, I believe. The Texan is not only a braggart about his acres, his oil, his wife's jewels and his share capital: he is also a deadeningly boorish boaster about his sexual prowess.

The Aussie who whacks you on the back during a schooner of ale in Sydney does not want to congratulate you on your swallow. He hopes to convince you of his virility before opening up the trap-door gambit: "Have I ever told you about the time . . .?" Ten to one what he tells you is biologically and physiologically impossible, but that won't stop him.

Even the Irishman has a nice line in self-flattery on this subject, which makes the pubs of O'Connell Street more entertaining than those "across the wather". But your Britisher is not usually given to such gross exaggeration. Much more frequently, he prefers to understate rather than overstate the facts of his physical experience.

Hence a great deal is not known about the more adventurous side of his amorous, intimate life.

Perhaps you remember the shrewd *canard* about the first things girls of different nationalities are apt to say after making love? Note that it was a *British* joke, invented *here* for *our* edification. It went something like this:

Mad'moiselle:	"You von't forget zat bracelet, vill you darleeng?"
Signorita:	"Seelly boy, of *course* I won't tell your bishop."
American Miss:	"And *what* did you say your name was?"
English Lady:	"D'you feel better now, darling?"

You see. The British *like* to see themselves as dreary bores in bed. It is they, or rather their novelists, who have unrelentingly insisted that Latins are *not* lousy lovers, and that American

8

women *are* as sexy as they like to sound and look. But all this is as much bunkum as is the notion that they themselves are romantically, sexually and maritally inferior.

Where is the proof of this? The proof, dear Brutus, *is* in ourselves. Everyone alive in these islands knows that he or she is as full of all the related complexities of warm blood, appraising eye, smooth phrase, and electric touch as any Mediterranean loafer or Californian gum-masticator.

Look at the record. Our popular Sunday press sells millions by reporting the romantic behaviour of English, Scottish, Welsh and Irish men and women in bed. However dull and bloodless our caresses may appear in public, or when portrayed by half-starved British actors and actresses (many of them more familiar with the polyglot seductions of Chelsea and the Earls Court Road than with a real piece of Anglo-Saxon persuasion), in private, they are all there.

The idea of this book is to give public evidence of this un-doubted fact. The *facts* in it are true. They are drawn from the record, from interviews and from already published material reflecting the habits and hazards of the British in bed.

As a structure for this tall order, I have chosen the twenty-four hours of the British lover's day, from "cock-crow", at the first pasty streak of dawn, right round the clock. Everything compressed into these chapters is part of our islands' contemporary folk history. But that is not my reason for writing it down.

I have set out to show that the British lover is much miscast on the world stage. He is *not* a feeble simpleton, largely incapable of satisfying his wife's sexual needs, or of finding visceral and financial stamina enough to keep a mistress. (There are, in fact, probably more illicit liaisons here than anywhere outside the free-loving Marquesas Islands.)

The sources used are mainly to be found published or quoted during the past five years or so. Only on rare occasions have I gone outside this contemporary enclave.

I am indebted to the *News of the World* for giving me access to their files and records; and to many other newspaper reports and reporters whose work I have enjoyed so much in the quiet retreat (were it not for the banging of the adjacent book-binders!) of the British Museum Newspaper Library at Colindale.

My grateful thanks are due to the following, who have kindly allowed me to reproduce their words and work: Norah Littlejohn, Sue Bickley, Nina Epton, David Malcolm, Michael Schofield, Clive Hirschhorn, Nell Dunn, Janet Suzman, Julie Christie,

Cyril Pearl, Marshall Pugh, Vic Sims, Susan Barnes, Peter Forbes, Peter Earle, Inge and Sten Hegeler, S. and G. B. Gale, Quentin Crewe and Gordon Rattray Taylor.

I should also like to acknowledge the valuable assistance and guidance given to me by Messrs Longmans, Green; Little, Brown & Co; MacGibbon & Kee; ABC Television; Merlin Press; Neville Spearman; Secker & Warburg; Cassell; Frederick Muller; and Thames and Hudson. And to the Editors of the *Daily Express*, the *Sunday Express*, the *Daily Mirror*, the *Sunday Mirror*, the *News of the World*, the *People*, *Reveille* and the *Daily Mail*, for the same reason.

And to the British lover and his mate, those much miscast hero-villains of our time, I offer the hope and the belief that both he and she will know better than to believe the slurs and calumnies about them which are given such prominence abroad. They will, I trust, recognize the truth when they see it here.

GERALD MCKNIGHT.
Grimaud, Var, 1966.

Chapter 1

4 a.m.

COCK-CROW

He couldn't sleep. He rolled out of bed cursing the drink Vicky had made him swallow the night before, pulling on some clothes with one hand, holding a cigarette with the other. Knowing he had to make the early plane to Paris, why had he stayed, instead of insisting on getting back to his own flat? Crazy. Thirty-nine, and in urgent need of having his head examined.

Others didn't do stupid **thi**ngs like this. Look at Jack, one of his best friends: settled, mature and successful. Happily married too, at least on the face of it. What had *he* got to show for his "fabulous" career in advertising, his "meteoric" gush to the top of the social and economic trees—and every other tree in sight? A good question, calling for a grim answer. Clive L...... thought about it while he squeezed some toothpaste on to a small, pink and unfamiliar toothbrush and examined his tongue in a softly lit bathroom mirror.

He was the father of two children he barely knew, often forgot and faintly disliked. His wife slept with every man who could be persuaded, at one of their parties, to ask her to meet him at the

Tate Gallery or somewhere. He'd lost track of the number of times he'd called up Ben, his solicitor, and later confided from the depths of a leather fortress at the Savile Club about her most recent outrage. Ben had never advised action, of course; probably because he'd known Clive didn't want any; just felt the need to fuss and get it off his neck that way.

But what made him put the brakes on before going over the edge with Angela was this: *he didn't know what she knew about him.* There was that silly letter Michele had written him from Weymouth. Its disappearance no longer frightened him, but it had never been explained; and of course he hadn't been able to ask about it. Then there were all the other little items, so many that he'd almost forgotten most of them. *But had she?*

Or was his wife systematically and secretly stock-piling all these fragments of his unfaithfulness like those women you read about in divorce cases? Against the day when—if he dared—he might raise his legal hand against *her*? He wouldn't put it past her. She was like her mother in certain ways; and Mrs V...... was a shrewd, crafty woman whose money was the sole badge of distinction between herself and the Yorkshire peasants she now patronized and mulcted, as tenants of her numerous small properties. In twenty years time, Clive reckoned, Angela would be the same.

But, it was hardly worth adding to the problem for this girl Vicky. She was not even attractive. He could see the three-quarter profile of her sleeping face in the mirror, now, because the bedlight was full on. They'd forgotten to switch it off last night when they fell asleep exhausted after their muddled bout of love-making. He thought about that.

She had wanted him from the start. Probably it was the flattery of this, he realized now, that had roused his own interest in this buxom typist with the broken, chewed finger nails. He couldn't imagine what else had brought him to this pitch.

Unless it was the proof it offered that he was *not* a waning power. She'd come up to him at the firm's party, the one Charles and Roger had given to celebrate the new Italian Presto table-salt account. "Excuse me," she had said in her harsh, flat voice which shrieked of Herne Hill Secondary Modern and the grey struggling crowds at Charing Cross suburban electric station. "The other girls were talkin' about you in the powder room, and I've been deputed to ask a, er, question."

"Oh?" He had given her the lofty, faintly-amused but warm-eyed expression he used for female clients and cocktail parties. "Well, what is it?"

She tried to look deadly serious, as though she was calling at his door with a thousand questions on his detergent habits for some market research group.

"They want to know if you sleep around." Snigger. *"Do you?"* For a moment he was not sure if she was pulling his leg; or if he had perhaps not heard her correctly. Then it sunk in that this pathetic mouse of a girl—he couldn't remember her name, even, at this minute; though he used her quite often from the typing pool and had mentally written her off because her ankles were thick and shapeless from behind—was asking him about his private, his most intimate, love-life.

He felt a flush of anger, then fear. Wouldn't do, he saw, to be too lordly about this. One or two of the other girls, he observed, were studiously pretending not to notice his conversation with— ah yes, he'd got it now—Miss A...... Vicky, or something equally obnoxious. But they were tuned in all right. He had to play it madly cool.

How? Did one lie quite soberly and say that one "didn't"? It sounded horribly square and prudish. Certainly wouldn't do his image any good, even if they believed him. And it was far more likely that they had proof to the contrary, supplied by an outside source. More than one of the girls he had "known" since he and Angela had given up trying to make it together was an ex-member of the staff. No doubt they kept up friendships; no woman could be trusted.

So? If he smirked and said, "But, of *course*!" wasn't that going to endanger his whole situation in the office? He'd be hopelessly compromised and they'd never let him forget it. It would soon reach Roger's sharp little pig's ears. And ten to one it would get back to Angela, via Charles, who was such a kind Dutch uncle to her.

No. The whole thing called for extreme tact and delicate handling. Fortunately he had managed to hold his face still while these thoughts were racing behind it. Now he smiled, in what he hoped was an enigmatic, wholly sophisticated, James-Bond-ish sort of way. "My dear Vicky," he told her, using his lowest vocal register and bending his head forward so that his strong wedge of sharply cut hair added youth and vigour to his features. "You must just *wait* and *see*, mustn't you?"

She held his gaze, smiling like a schoolgirl who had asked a

13

boy to dance and been accepted. "Why not?" she said. "I'm not doing anything better, am I?"

He looked at the glass of gin and orange she was holding. "Sure you haven't been drinking too much?" he asked, twinkling his eyes to de-fuse the snub. She shook her head, still looking up into his eyes with the same curiously grave, immature smile. "No? Then let's talk this over, Vicky. You'd better get your coat."

He was obeying some force, or habit, stronger than his normal judgement. He was being conned, that was obvious. But something almost pathetic about this little suburban waif made him follow the path she had brutally invited him to take her on.

"I'm leaving, anyway," he told her. "Just wait while I collect my brief-case. We'll get a taxi and find somewhere to eat; okay?"

"Okay. I'm hungry."

"So am I. We'll go to the . . ." he almost said Mirabelle, which he used almost exclusively for these occasions; then changed his mind, because he was worried about her suitability ". . . to the new fish place in Soho," he said. "Have you ever had a rose in a brandy glass served with your meal? That's what's in store for you."

"Sounds super," she said, giggling. His spirits sank a little, then; but it was over dinner that he knew what he was really in for. She was *everything* he despised: parochial, dull, arbitrary and implacably anti- all things which would not fit exactly into the mould of her tiny life. It was with the greatest effort—and a second large Armagnac—that he was able to restore something of the soft glow of warmth she had imparted at her first bald, bold approach during the party.

"Did the others really put you up to this?" he asked her.

"Oh, yes." She looked mischievous. "Why? Are you scared I'll tell them what you said?"

"What did I say?"

"Only that I must wait and see."

"And must you?"

She shrugged. "That's up to you, isn't it?" she said.

He made a final, unwelcome decision. "Come on." He took her arm as they got up. "My car's outside and there's time for a nightcap at my club."

She didn't ask what he meant by "club", she followed him meekly through the cold, empty lobby of the block of flats where he could always book into a guest room, at any hour of the day or night, with no questions asked. (And with only a fiver to pay

14

when they sent him the bill under private cover to his office.)

The bottle of scotch which the restaurant's wine waiter had let him have as a special, well-compensated favour warmed them. In the soft, cosy light of the small divan room he found he could enter into the spirit of the occasion easily enough. But at first he did not want to touch her.

She sat at his feet on the thick pile of the beige wall-to-wall carpet and rested her head on his knees. He found the pose embarrassing, as though she was silently rebuking him for being so unmanly. At last, when she had filled his glass for the third time and he had downed the strong scotch-and-water in one go, he found the desire—the almost impersonal, anonymous desire— for her soft, plump body.

How many other petty lecheries are roughing up the consciences of these islands' awakening inhabitants at this hour? How many more are there like Clive, wishing in fruitless impotence that the passions of a bewitching night had spared them? It is no good saying now that the whole thing was sordid and disgraceful. Not the slightest point in shutting it out of mind and heart. These deeds are done. The sins of the night have already mortgaged the days ahead. They demand payment in the hardest currency of all: human happiness. Man digs his grave on earth with the same weapon that gives the earth fresh life; desire is a siren strumpet mourning at his grave.

"But what *is* it about English (or British, if you prefer it) gentlemen?" she asked of her typewriter. Alone in her Kensington flat, the curtains drawn against the street light outside, the famous woman's magazine writer sat putting her thoughts on paper. On this subject, particularly, she was well worth listening to:

"What is so *awful* about them is that they will share their beds sooner than their minds," she tapped out briskly. "For a woman, it is so degrading if she cannot be regarded other than as a carcase."

She paused, puffed at a cigarette and looked soberly at the furniture of her bedroom. "One very often feels," she wrote, "like a chest-of-drawers. Or rather like the contents of one, tiny drawer in such a thing.

"Because Englishmen keep their smallest hobbies—the trivia of their lives—in the top right-hand drawer. And their women and sex in the other.

15

"What really matters to them—the important considerations of work, money and sport—occupy the remaining large drawers. To survive in this country, believe me, we women have practically to *become* men."

A fit of coughing interrupted her narrative, but the famous writer was well into her stride. She rapped on:

"It is *we* who pay the bills and mend the fuses these days, while the man becomes increasingly ornamental. It would not be so bad if they would only treat us as intelligent human beings, and admire our new-found capacities.

"But take this weekend ritual in the suburbs, when every Englishman feels a compulsion to clean his motorcar. I believe they get an extraordinary private joy out of doing it. It is a form of peacock feathers, don't you know. They want to strut about in full view of neighbours; not actually work. Work is for women, even the unglamorous business of cleaning the car's insides. That's left to her.

"Sports cars are another thing. Most of the men who run the raciest are half-impotent. It's what the brain boys call a "compensation mechanism" or whatever it is; something to make up for their much deeper inadequacies.

"We women notice these things. Because we see the boys close to. The *real* boys, you know. Why it never gets out is because we can't comment. They've cut off our tongues ...

"The publishers of women's magazines? All men. And the women editors are securely muzzled. It's the chappies behind them, in the huge offices higher up in the building somewhere, who set the underlying themes. They talk *for* the women.

"Oh, I know Englishmen are considerate, and intelligent and so on. But as lovers there's so *much* they don't have. So very much. I can think of at least six really terrible weaknesses of theirs.

"Firstly, they're so *bloody* conceited. Ask one of them in for a drink after he's given you a lift home, if you're a girl, and see what I mean. He'll *automatically* assume this is an invitation to make a pass.

"Because they're so *unsubtle*. They don't bother with any preliminaries. No approach. No warm-up at all. That sort of thing is lost on them. Indeed some of them, I'm sure, still believe in *droit de seigneur*.

"And *mean*. Oh, they have mistresses all right. But don't imagine they *keep* them. It's far more likely the poor girls keep *them*! And almost certainly they pay their own rent, buy their

16

own clothes and have to help out with bills in restaurants.

"What is so maddening about that is that these chappies still think they should have the right to drop in for a "quicky" whenever the mood catches them. It never seems to occur to them that the girlies might like a little something to make them feel good; a tiny present, or anything to show they thought of them. Not they.

"The tragedy of my generation, which grew out of World War I, is that there are at least two million of us women surplus. There aren't enough men of our age to go round, so we have to be jolly careful before we send them packing. They might be the last remaining grub-provider!

"But what I really find so trying, personally, is that they are so fearfully *square*. You won't believe it, but when one gallant English gentleman, long ago, made a pass at me, he actually said: 'You see, my wife doesn't understand me.'

"And when I told my papa about it, expecting him to be terribly amused, he only said: 'But isn't that what one says? I always do.'

"They're *inhibited*, that's another thing. The way they drink gives them away, have you noticed it? That's what really ruins them as lovers.

"Because an Englishman in love is usually so shy he has to gulp down drink after drink before daring to go into action. Then, unless he's very experienced, or lucky, he probably over-does it and ends up incapable.

"*That's* why so many Englishmen find themselves in the most absurd plight known to lovers. They embarrass and hurt a woman who may have felt the beginnings of love for them. They tread all over her ego and self-esteem by ending up quite unable to perform at all. All they get out of it is a hangover and a cue for another of their ghastly apologies.

"Yes, and lastly they are such terrifying *moral cowards*. When an American is unfaithful to his wife, he probably breaks down and weeps afterwards. Blubs openly. Then begs to know 'what'll I tell Ethel?' He may even show you snapshots of his kids in Connecticut.

"But the Englishman has no guilt. He may protest, 'I've-never-been-unfaithful-and-I-never-will.' But apart from this flat lie, he probably won't mention his wife at all. Or he'll talk about her with the awful, clammy sort of affection that gives a mistress guilt feelings right up her spine.

"For some extraordinary reason, danger seems to be tied up

with sex for the English. Why else would all those couples lie about doing it so brazenly in public places like Hyde Park? They're far worse than anything I've seen in Paris.

"It's very noticeable in queers too. Partly, I suppose, because they're criminals for some absurd reason. I know a couple who'd both been to prison; but they would keep on importuning in public lavs, where they were sure to be caught sooner or later.

"When I asked why, they explained that it gave them far more *thrill*. And *potency*. Isn't that interesting?

"The danger of getting caught was a sort of mainspring for their sex. Perhaps there's something in that. Isn't it what is getting more and more into the English teenagers, too?"

The famous magazine writer took the paper out of her machine, read what she had written, laughed, and tore it up.

It is all this frozen, canned and synthetic food you feed your men on. It is not doing them any good. They are dull, sluggish, fading away and not a bit gay.

> *Comment by Australian girl, reported by*
> *Norah Littlejohn in* REVEILLE

The British male is on the decline. He used to be virile and handsome, gallant and strong. He looked masculine and he followed masculine pursuits ... Where is he now—this masculine British male?

The men of today are wearing necklaces and bracelets, pointed shoes and frilled shirts. They are having their hair permed, blow-waved and even tinted. They are learning to knit and sew and to darn their own socks. In their leisure time they watch television or worse!—play bingo ... The British male, in fact, is becoming a cissy.

> *Sue Bickley in* REVEILLE

A cissy? Think again, Miss Bickley. One of our most patient and respected researchers, Geoffrey Gorer, finds that *nearly half* the married Englishmen he has questioned have had love affairs outside marriage.

The famous British writer on world love habits, Nina Epton, has had to admit (though grudgingly) that "While it is a little too early to be able to consult memoirs and diaries of twentieth-century English lovers ... there are plenty of indications that this century will not be deficient in Great Lovers."*

And in his publish-and-be-damned book *Eros Denied*, Wayland Young (the Earl of Kennet) comments: ". . . the boy or girl who has had a certain number of affairs before marriage will find it

*Love and the English (Cassell).

18

hard to stop having them afterward, and must either put up with the tensions of adultery or else consciously find a means of avoiding it. Advancing age helps, but not soon enough."

It may not be true that if you scratch a British male you'll find a Casanova struggling to get out. But it's a downright lie to say he's no lover at all.

As one chap said to another in their local one evening: "Do you ever talk to your wife when you're making love, old boy?" And as the other chap answered, with typically British candour: "Yes, *if there's a phone handy.*"

Chapter 2

5 a.m.

BEAT THE CLOCK

For the most part, Britain's lovers are rubbing the sleep out of their awakening eyes at this hour. Or working out the last enchanted moments of a dream fantasy. Or merely lying unconscious. All over slumbering semi-land, in the pretentious glory of the stockbrokers' double-fronted pseudo-tudors, right the way up to the forty-guinea-a-night Maharajah Suite at the Mayfair Hotel in London, W.1., dawn is taking over; the night shift is pulling out.

A vast, swelling chorus of hated alarm clocks is jangling. Hands are reaching out for them, groping for their silencer buttons, knocking them over, shoving them still ringing under pillows; ignoring them and even flinging them at innocent walls. Nevertheless, the alarms are winning.

Workers are being dragged out of warm reveries, even warmer covers. Being sucked free of caresses. Being driven, grey-faced, toward tea-and-toast breakfasts after a geyzer-heated sluice in a myriad cracked basins; a quick stroke with the family toothbrush.

The stoking of a million solid-fuel boilers is colder, at this hour, than a royal snub.

As a multitude of hybrid cats are let inside back doors to purr over saucers of icy milk, the teeth of this British day have begun to gnash. We shall watch it well from our place in the shadows. Maybe it will produce a number of surprises for those of us who think nothing much happens in this quiet, quaint land of ours.

For the moment, let us ask a question fundamental to this hour, when everyone and everything but the incorrigible cocks seem to be groping and part-confused: What, to a British man and woman on this particular morning in the nineteen-sixties, is love?

Something you can't never get at to scratch, the nursemaids used to define it, rocking their prams in Windsor Great Park. Like "linen often chang'd", wrote the poet Phineas Fletcher. Or "like the measles", as Jerome Klapka Jerome said, adding "we all have to go through it".

Whatever it is, nineteen-year-old Fred F...... was in the grip of it at 5.12 on this particular morning. He walked like a man stiff from unaccustomed exercise. His hands were thrust deep in the trouser pockets of his best suit; an Italian-style, sixteen-quid affair in mauvy-brown. His feet, in sawn-off winkle-pickers, hardly sounded on the dew-damp paving stones of Paradise Road.

"It's now or never," he kept saying, not very originally, in his thoughts. "Now or never. *I've got to have her!*"

The gate of No. 47 stuck firm against his push. He used his knee, bending the swollen wood from the post until it gave. The tiny pit of a garden, hemmed in by sparkling wet privet, was black as a tomb. He felt the key blank, sharp at the edges from having been freshly cut, under his fingers. Then it was in the Yale, turning easily.

For an instant his heart threatened to knock him out with its shocked beat. The hall smelt of *people*. It smelt of Joe, whose overcoat hung on the wall-rack just inside the door. It seemed a gross invasion of privacy to go inside. He had to force himself.

Then he was groping towards the stairs, guided by the light from the small window at their head. He climbed them easily, the foam underlay muffling his tread. Alice and Joe's bedroom was dead ahead, he knew.

The moment he turned the glazed handle, the door opened and he heard her breathing. Heavy and regular, ending in a fine, resonant snore. He stood a while where he was in the doorway, waiting for the thin percolation of light from the landing to reflect the contents of the room.

She was lying on the far side of the double bed, empty on his side. Watching, he was fascinated by her expansion and contraction as the deep breaths came and went. Then he closed the door. Carefully, standing where he was, he took off first one and then the other shoe.

He put them on the floor beside his feet. Still standing, he began to undress. His coat, trousers, shirt and tie dropped in a heap on top of the shoes. Fred, in his underwear, took a last look at the sleeping figure of Alice M......, his best friend's wife, and then got in beside her.

Which is as far as this hour will allow us to follow the fortunes of Mrs M...... and her uninvited guest. Will Fred, or Alice, get the shock of their young lives? We will return to them later.

Meanwhile, back to the subject of love (which in some strange way *must* have been Fred's motivation; as much as it was Romeo's when Juliet—more obligingly than Alice, it's true—allowed the ivy to be ladder to his ardour).

Just as it inspired Freud to tell us that "we owe the fairest flowers of our love life to the reaction against the hostile impulse which we divine in our breasts," so we must expect violence and sex and love to be bed-fellows. We may not *like* it, but the statistics do not lie.

"Out of every sixteen babies born in England and Wales during 1961, one was illegitimate." Thus declared a recent statistical review. "In the major cities, the percentage was higher. In London, *one out of every eight born was illegitimate.*"

Who cares?

"Somewhere, somehow, sometime, someone's gonna be kissed . . .," as the singers used to tell us not so long ago.

Or, as St Paul advised the Corinthians, in fewer words: "love never faileth". It never faileth to get young girls with babies, if they don't keep a tight hold on the reins of passion. Was it not the poet Swinburne who warned: "No thorns go as deep as a rose's, And love is more cruel than lust."?

Somebody should have drummed this into poor, twelve-year-old Margie B...... before the first lightening of the darkness in the bedroom she shared with her mother in their village on Salisbury Plain. It woke her up to the agony of another day.

Her first thought on waking was that it wasn't morning yet. She had temporarily forgotten and was back in the happiness of knowing that she could lie abed a while longer. The feeling made her drowsy and joyful.

But even as it filled her the happiness seemed to warn her half-asleep mind not to take it too seriously. And the quick thump in her stomach, under the flannelette pyjamas, completed her awakening.

"Oh my God," she thought, *"it's alive already."*

It was four months since Ron had taken her to the old forge by the river bank. Had carried her satchel and pushed her bike with one arm. The other was round her blazer, helping her avoid the ochre puddles sunk in the rutted track.

She hadn't meant to let him.

Like her mother said, she was a good girl. "I don't have to worry over you, Margie," Mrs B...... had told her more than once. "Not like the others. I know you can look after yourself. You're *sensible*."

She was sensible, all right. The way some of the other girls at school carried on she thought disgusting. To hear them talk, anyone would have imagined they let whole armies of boys kiss and cuddle them.

Especially in the pictures, in Marketon, which Margie and all the girls and boys went to on Saturday nights, taking the Blue Bus from outside their one general store. But Margie had never been like that.

Why had it been different with Ron? She didn't know, and even trying to analyse it made her feel sick. She didn't let herself think about love, because a girl of twelve wasn't supposed to feel that for a boy.

She was too young. Even though the sight of him thrilled her to ecstasy. And the feel and smell of his jacket gave her a flow of warmth, safety and protection.

She barely remembered her father. But Ron was the first ever to make her forget him altogether. The afternoon it happened, after hockey, she wasn't thinking of anything but the joy of having a man's arms round her.

On the other side of the little bedroom, her mother's breathing was even and soft. Would she, Margie thought, have to kill herself and the baby at the same time? It flashed through her mind, with a jab of real fear, that she had not finished her homework.

Whatever would Miss Evans say?

The scientific facts about love are few and reasonably well-known. It causes loss of appetite, sleep and weight. When it takes an unhappy turn, it predisposes its victims to infection by the germs of tuberculosis . . .

"The Winning Art", David Malcolm

The cold woke Matthew R. . . . . . . The cold and the gnawing pain in his hip bone from lying on the floor. Where the duffle coat covered him, he was clammily warm. But the long extremities of his thin body stuck out.

The gas fire, still with two good burners, was empty of flame. He cursed it, turning the stiff, brass tap full on. Last night, when they'd put the shilling in, Marcia had said it would last if they turned it down.

There was no hiss from the fire and he pushed it off savagely. Then he rubbed his chilled hands together. Marcia, a heap of coats and clothing, with her head in a crumpled food carton, seemed unnaturally still.

He was shivering. And his teeth hurt where the filling had fallen out the night before. That was when they'd eaten the last tin of meat loaf with the salted spaghetti.

Before the fight . . .

He looked round the bare room, expecting chaos. In the pale, filtering dawn-light from the naked windows, it was peaceful. But one of the wooden chairs was on its back, legs sticking up like a dead animal's. Abstractedly, he counted three. Then he remembered what he had done with the fourth.

It gave him a queer start to think about it now. She had fallen when he hit her. After a while, when he'd cooled down, he'd touched her with his foot. And she'd spoken, telling him she was all right.

Should he have given her that shot which had started the whole thing? It was lousy "horse", they both knew that. Max couldn't be trusted. And anyway they hadn't been able to give enough in the way of guarantee.

That powder compact of her mother's may have been silver, but it wouldn't fetch much. Like a cold nail in his head, the worry of getting more supplies of heroin for the days ahead bored into him.

He must have some soon. Last night's had been only enough to give him a hangover appetite. And there was Marcia to think of. She'd need plenty, if he'd really hurt her head.

He went over to her. Where he could see the ends of dark hair he pulled some of the tangled jerseys and a man's jacket away, remembering how he had thrown them over her before collapsing

24

into sleep. Her face looked ghastly. A line of dried blood ran from the lower corner of her mouth onto the crumpled cardboard of her makeshift pillow. Before he touched her he thought she was dead. Then she sat up. "Christ," she said.

Teenagers with the most sexual experience were also those with the most money to spend and therefore the quarry for the very active salesmen of the teenage commercial market. Incidentally the only group of teenagers that sets out to resist the blandishments of the marketeers are the Beats, and they come in for an extra measure of social hostility.

*"The Sexual Behaviour of Young People",
Michael Schofield (Longmans)*

"In a way it's the biggest problem we have to face," said Whitechapel youth club leader Yogi Mayer thoughtfully. "A boy and a girl in love *ought* to feel at home in their local youth club. But how many do?"
Interview

Precisely at this moment, 200 miles to the west, Miss Milk Bottle Top of 1965 was grunting indignantly. Her companion was getting up. And when Jonny Sunbeam took his sixteen-and-a-half stone of packed bone, sinew and oiled flesh off the mattress, no amount of sophisticated springing could compensate entirely for the loss.

Jonny was still asleep, the alarm only ringing in the back of his head. He punched the top of it with a finger broken in the bout with Man-eater Jack Jones. It stopped. Then he flopped a massive leg over the side of the bed and sat up, blinking.

"Wo-time-sit?" he growled, yawning, scratching his shoulder and batting eyelids the size and thickness of medium-done entrecotes. Nobody answered. Miss M-B-T turned over, away from him, grabbing a firm fistful of bedding as she did so. Jonny ignored her. He went to the window, ripped back the heavy curtains, pushed up the heavy sash with one hand and inhaled the murky morning air noisily.

After five expansive breaths, he began to limber up. Arms and legs were stretched, shaken and flexed. A lot of patting and pinching went on. At times he would drop into a wrestler's pose and grunt convincingly. The girl in the bed, who had decided she couldn't sleep with all this going on, watched him balefully out of a thin, pretty face.

"Pity you didn't win," she said sarcastically, during an uncomfortable exercise in which Mr Sunbeam locked hands behind

25

his back and tugged in both directions. "All this training."

He unlocked the arms and turned to look at her.

"'ow could I?" he asked in a high, boyish voice. "You make too many demands on me. That's what it is. That's what did it, I can tell you."

She sniffed. The contempt was obvious. "Not that it gets me nowhere," she said. "When was the last time?"

He looked darkly at her, his head lowered like a wounded bull. "You're always on about it, aren't you? Can't think of nothing else, can you? What's the matter with you? Why can't you find something else to take your mind off it?"

She dilated her eyes, very wide. "It's not *my* mind, I'm sure," she said. "There's nothing wrong with *my* mind. *Or* what's in it. If you find the subject so revoltin', I wonder you bother to bring it up."

He turned back to the window and, after two small jerks of his torso in the way of preparation, suddenly swung himself down until his dark tousled head was between his legs, both arms twined round his calves and ankles. From this position he could view her, upside down. His voice sounded strained and distant.

"It's right what they say about marriage," he said mournfully. "It's a farce."

HE: "Do you know the world's shortest bed-time story?"
SHE: "No."
HE: "That's it."

Chapter 3

6 a.m.

MORNING GLORY

It is now time to be getting up. Or sleeping in. However, it is
as well to know that lovers are still alive. Even if rubble and
stray dogs and street cleaners are making free with the plinth
of Eros in Piccadilly Circus. Even if Lady Godiva's immodesty
on her Coventry statue is wrapped in dewy darkness; and,
nearby, Peeping Tom suffers eye-strain.

Particularly so if Nottingham's stone lions, said to roar whenever a virgin passes, lie dumb as wooden waiters.

Why, you might almost think the passions of the British night
were suffering a tidal change at this strange hour. Or would
you . . .

Detective-Sergeant Hubert L. . . . . . could make out nothing
more interesting from the first floor window than the darkened
shapes of the terraced buildings on the other side of Etna Street,
W.1. His thoughts were not on these. He was peering out only
in an attempt to cool his brain which would persist in running
on parallel but widely divided lines.

As the clock in a church somewhere over in the Bayswater Road direction struck the hour of six he was thinking:

How much will the old girl go to, if I *really* press her? Easy there, Bert . . . don't drive her too hard. Remember what happened to Henry. Watch it, mate—she's cost more coppers their stripes than you've had hot dinners. But twenty nicker wasn't what I'd bargained for! What about her girls? Surely those cards on the board outside the newsagent's in Ponting Street were enough to shop them all. "Learn to twist with all the most exciting positions" eh? Even that dim bastard of a magistrate, Monty, ought to get that lot . . .

So ran one side of the dialogue. The other, the reason why he had turned to the window, was more disturbing.

Nice pair of legs on that dark one. Did she fancy him? She wouldn't sit there, cross-legged and with her skirt up around her arse if she didn't, would she? Well, why not ask to have a word with them all alone in the other room, then have her sent in first? The old cow ought to be glad to let him have a bit on the side. Cows! All of them. Made him sick. None of them were going to make a fool of him, especially at this hour of the bloody morning. But that one did have a nice pair. No doubt about that. He was afraid to turn round and look at them. But he couldn't go on looking out of this bleeding window all day, could he?

"What about this bloke, then?" he said nastily, turning towards the four girls sitting round the low coffee table in the middle of the room. "How kinky is he?"

The dark one who fancied him, as he thought, answered. But first she sinuously recrossed her legs so that her nigger-brown nylon tops showed. "He's all the way. Bent double," she said in a flat, Birmingham voice. Then she giggled. "Tell him, Clarice," she said.

A beehive blonde, intently painting her nails, looked at her listlessly. "Ow, 'im," she said, "'e's about the kinkiest one I've ever 'ad. But . . ." she wriggled her buttocks on the gilt chair like a petulant child, ". . . suits me. 'e don't want much."

"Go on," said the girl in the corner of the sofa. She was wearing riding breeches, boots and spurs and reading a teenage girl's comic. "What's he make you do?"

Clarice examined her nails, holding them up to the light. She

Seemed satisfied. "'aven't I told you?" she asked. "'e's daft, really. Some sort of a bigshot lawyer, so Ma'am says, and can't 'ave it unless 'e's flogged." She laughed harshly, and the laughter made her cough. Detective-Sergeant Leyland shifted his eyes away as her shortie housecoat of soft, pink mohair fell wide apart.

"Oh, murder," gasped Clarice. "Where was I? Oh yes, this 'ere kinky feller. Well, it's just that we 'ave to bring 'im 'ere, 'andcuffed . . ." she looked saucily at the detective. "Like you, mate," she scoffed, "only a bloody sight better, I should think."

All the girls laughed. "Shame," said the dark one. "Don't tease him, Clarice. He's nice. Anyway, what then?"

Clarice had taken the brush out of the bottle of puce enamel and was stroking wet paint over the nails which had dried. "We meet by appointment," she said in a bored, sing-song voice. "'e tips Ma'am off which train 'e's going to be on. Then I and Cynth 'ave to be on the platform waitin' for 'im when 'e gets off." She giggled again. "Oh, I dunno," she said. "It's daft."

"Go on," urged the girl in riding breeches, "what happens?"

"Oh." She dipped the brush back into the tiny glass pot and stirred vigorously. "Well, then we 'ave to escort 'im all the way back 'ere. Didn't you know?"

"Me? No."

"Well we do. And Ma'am puts on that black gown and wig 'e's given 'er. She 'as to *sentence* 'im!"

All the girls shrieked with laughter.

"Don't ask me what it does to 'im, but 'e's as docile as a lamb while it's all goin' on. Then we 'ave to, you know . . ." She looked blank-eyed at the girl on the sofa.

"You mean you have to beat him?"

"Course. Well, I mean, some of them kinkies can't get enough of that sort of thing, can they? Heh, Dawn, what about that one what wanted you to kick 'im downstairs?"

The fourth girl was eating a sandwich with slow, grave movements of her knife and fork. She smirked. "That's right," she said in a baby voice. "He did, too. Only I said it was bad for me 'eart."

The girls giggled and a look passed between them.

The door into the dimly-lit room had opened. A plump woman, her shortness accentuating the pale width of her neck, came up to the table. She was smoking a short cigar. "Mr L......," she said in a cultured voice. "Would you like to come into the office?"

Englishmen and Englishwomen strike me as so unsuited to each other that really I wonder if they ought ever to meet at all.

Honor Tracy

A proof of an inside feature page of the *Daily Express* lay on the subs' table where it had been tossed during the night's production. It was covered with circles of damp canteen tea from the night's cups. As the cleaner with bright peroxide hair tied up under a gay scarf leaned on her brush she could read some of the main piece. It was a column by Mr Robin Douglas-Home. "Any British lady," she read, "of high birth worth her hormones has her first serious love affair with a horse . . ."

"Blimey," she said. Then, raising her voice, she called over to a dark, squat woman on her hands and knees, scrubbing. "Ay, Glad," she said. "Did y'know them debs 'ad it orf with their 'orses?"

"Garn!"

"That's what it says 'ere." She read on, fascinated. Mr Douglas-Home continued: "And from that moment on the proximity of a horse seems to act as a powerful aphrodisiac."

The cleaner's eyes clouded, then skipped to the final paragraph. "Speaking for myself, though," she read, "I think I'd honestly prefer to be a hunted fox rather than find myself dancing fetlock to fetlock with a typical English huntswoman."

"Cor, filthy ol' monkey!" she said. She laughed. Then she crumpled the proof into a ball and put it into a purple sack of waste paper she had at her feet. Her eyes went to the electric clock over the News Editor's desk. "'ere, Glad, love, time we was gorn. It's six-bleeding-thirty."

. . . Bad taste, and the unhappiness which it feeds, are also a part of love.

"The Winning Art", by David Malcolm

He lay awake looking at the ceiling and thinking of how he had heard this young actress, Julie Christie, who was such a knock-out in *Billy Liar*, talking about herself over a glass of black Mackeson in a Birmingham pub. "Quite a few men," she had said, "have been in love with me, or said they have been. And I suppose I *could* fall in love. But I feel quite unable to think of myself getting married—really married, with a cottage, and kids and all that."

She'd looked puzzled. "I don't know what it is with me,"

she'd tried to explain to the fellow with the note-book, sitting with her. This was before she'd become really famous and he was the only journalist. "I like men—lovely, long-haired men. Hair's so pretty, don't you think? But somehow I get fed up. And where I'm dreadfully selfish is in taking everything I can to make *me* happy without caring about the pain it may cause others."

The man in bed closed his eyes, wondering what sort of man she would marry one day. Or if she'd change her mind. (N.B. today, Julie says: "My whole attitude to the subject has changed. If nothing else, I've learnt since then about giving as well as taking. Although I wouldn't go back on the 'I like men . . .' sentence.") Perhaps it would be one of those actor types. Or a tycoon, like that model Fiona something. He switched on the bedside light and found the paper with it in.

"I asked her," he read, under a picture of the Baroness Fiona von Thyssen, "what she thought about Englishmen and about the possibility of marrying one. She shook her head and smiled. "Uh-huh, I love England, and if I didn't have two children to raise I'd probable settle in London. But I *cannot*, repeat cannot, take Englishmen."

Couldn't she now? He read on, grinning. "I think they're the most insensitive bunch of punks that ever drew breath. They make absolutely no attempt to understand the way a girl's mind works. They're selfish and unsubtle and generally about as charming as a rattlesnake. No," she said very definitely, "you can keep your Englishmen. I'd almost go so far as to say that it's *because* of them I left England."

He raised his eyebrows and turned over a fold in the paper. There was no stopping the Baroness. "I think they all believed," she continued, "just because I was a model, that I'd be easy prey. Well, they were wrong. But I suppose it's one of the occupational hazards of the profession."

The article, in the *Sunday Express*, was signed "By Clive Hirschhorn." Ha! thought William A......, in bed in South Shields, what did *she* know about being married to an Englishman? He nudged the woman next to him, and she grunted.

"Ask Mary if she'll make the tea, there's a dear," he said gently. Then he got up and put on his trousers. He liked these trousers. They were neatly pressed and soft against his skin. He'd always had a sensitive skin, like his mother who couldn't bear sunburn.

"Did you want one egg or two?" Vera asked him, from the

bed. She was never sure. Even when he let her pour, she couldn't seem to remember how many lumps he took. Though she'd been with him and Mary now for nearly two years, when Bobby was only eighteen months old.

"Just one will do nicely," he said. "I'll be quick shaving."

He went out onto the landing and tapped on the door opposite. "Mary?" he called. "Are you up, love?" His wife's sleepy voice answered. He wasn't sure whether she had said "coming" or "come in". He stood undecided.

The door opened and she came out, a short woman still comely though with greying hair and deep lines in her face. Her eyes were dark as a gipsy's. "Morning, love," she said, her hands going to her hair instinctively. "Don't forget it's Vera's turn to do the breakfast, will you?"

"She's doing it now. Did you sleep well?"

She looked at him curiously out of her black, sexy eyes. "What time did you leave?" she asked. "I didn't hear you. Must have been asleep."

"Aye," he said. "Well, Vera said she was cold."

"That's all right." She said it as though she wanted to make him understand that she had not been accusing him of deserting her. "*You* know it is." She laughed, playfully. "Just so long as you're happy, eh, sweetypie?"

"Go on with you," he said. He gave her a shove and she went, chuckling, back into her room. He opened the bathroom door and disappeared inside. At least she didn't have to get his breakfast now Vera was living with them, that was something.

It was a funny way of carrying on. He supposed some people would think it indecent, even disgusting, for a man to live with his wife and his mistress and *both* their children by him under the one roof. But it suited him, his wife Mary and Vera very well indeed.

As a matter of fact, Mary hadn't had so much done for her since Edward, the first of their children, was born. And she had had four others since then. He heard her now, as he turned on the hot tap for his shaving water.

"*V-e-r-a!*" she called down the stairs, over the sound of the knocking in the pipes. "Wait a mo', love, and I'll come down and mak' th' tea."

The suggestion that delinquency represents a failure to achieve a social life organised round sexual interest is advanced by Dr T. C. N. Gibbens, senior lecturer in forensic psychiatry at London University, in a preliminary report of a psychiatric investigation of Borstal boys published today.

"We read much about delinquent areas, delinquent subcultures, and why delinquents join gangs, but less about why the delinquent does not have girl friends like most of his non-delinquent contemporaries and organise his social life round them," he says.

Criminologists had considered "broken homes" and "maternal deprivation" systematically, but few attempts had been made to relate sexual behaviour and development to criminal behaviour. It was found that 46 per cent of the boys had no experience of heterosexual intercourse; 37 per cent had occasional experience, and 17 per cent were promiscuous. Four per cent of the boys admitted to homosexual interests, but 25 per cent had known or suspected homosexual tendencies. The vast majority of boys said they did not drink or seldom did so.

THE TIMES, *7 February 1963.*

As Brian L...... turned towards his wife Alicia in their £300 Heal's honeymoon bed the clock in the village church tower was beginning to chime the hour of six. Alicia shivered slightly. "Oh my God, not again," she murmured. Then his silk-pyjama-ed arms were round her. "Darling, you'll enjoy it this time, really you will," he whispered. She turned on her back helplessly.

Chapter 4

7 a.m.

FOR THE BIRDS

By seven in the morning the British Cupid is capricious, dangerous and hostile. Men who have spent the night with women not
their wives are fumbling for words to overcome their feelings of
disgust. A commercial traveller in Derby pats the chambermaid
on her bare bottom and says through a smoker's cough: "What
about a cuppa, luv?"

Whores are asleep and alone. In Etna Street the girls have
dropped into bed, sighing with fatigue, while Detective-Sergeant
Hubert L...... talks to Ma'am behind the closed doors of her
"office". All over Britain women are lying with men and dreaming of other men. Husbands, too, are on their backs in wakefulness and day-mares; listening to the rasping snores of their wives;
planning divorces, separations, holidays alone and homicides.
Behind the new laundromat in an East Anglian town a strangely
thin figure in an unkempt garden is filling a freshly dug grave.

Two consenting homosexuals in Surrey are feeding their cat,
a fat monster, and getting ready to deliver bread and eggs to

the villagers their dairy serves, while arguing over the ballet they saw last night on television.

Young men in love are dreaming of racing cars in British Green plunging over the embankment at Sebring. The girls they love are awake, planning what they will wear on their wedding days. And plotting the future careers of these fiancés, with mental notes to get rid of "that *frightful* sports car".

It is 7 a.m. A lousy hour for lovers. Really only for the birds.

And all this while, Fred F...... was lying in a cold sweat. The bed was warm. Alice's back was towards him and she was still deeply asleep. But the thought of what could happen when she woke up chilled him.

It was irrational, he knew. Joe had assured him she was game for anything. He tried to believe it now, tried to tell himself he'd be all right just as long as he didn't *seem* nervous.

And he knew she liked him. He had read it in her eyes a dozen times, when he and Joe and her had been out at the pubs together. Or at a dance.

Indeed, it hadn't only been the photos Joe had shown him at the works. Though they had started the fuse burning in his mind. Even now, as he thought of them, they touched off a muscle of desire.

What was it Joe had said? "You can do anything with her, Fred boy. She's a ruddy bitch on heat when she gets going. Look at this picture, then, if you don't believe me. She posed for that!"

The photographs were unbelievable. Not human. Strangely distorted, with grotesque interminglings of crooked limbs and gaping, darkened crevices. Fred had never seen anything like them.

Whenever he met her after that he found it hard to keep the blood out of his cheeks. And lying in bed at night and on Sunday mornings he invented erotic fantasies about her. In them, he was doing the things to Alice that he had seen her acquiescing to in the pictures.

Then when Joe's keys fell out of his pocket in the locker room at the works, the idea had started. Why not take the plunge? She couldn't very well egg him on while Joe was about. And he might never find a chance to be properly alone with her.

But if he was to drop in one morning after Joe had left—as he had to do at 4.30 a.m. every morning, Fred well knew—well, she was a woman, wasn't she? And if those pictures and Joe's lascivious comments were anything to go by, a ripe one at that.

He had the keys back in Joe's pocket, and a copy made, before the break was over. There was nothing much more to it. He called in on them one night, ostensibly to ask if they'd like to come out to the pub with him for a drink to celebrate his birthday. That was all the opportunity he needed to test the blank and see that it worked. It did, a treat.

He didn't at first believe he'd go through with it, but after a while it grew on him. And the key gave him a touch of power. So this morning, when he'd woken early, he'd come up to the corner, really to see if he had guts enough.

From the shadow of the Church door he'd watched Joe depart, shoulders hunched against the misty cold. Then he'd done it.

But now? Now he was dead scared, like a rabbit in a stoat's path. It was getting on for seven, and she hadn't stirred. He didn't dare to touch her, or to move. Even if he'd wanted to run, now, he didn't have the courage to do so.

It was just as he was thinking what the foreman would say if he didn't get to his bench by 7.30 that he felt her move, stretch and begin to turn towards him.

Leaves, mould, mushrooms, mosses . . . very **er**otic.

H.R.H. the Princess Margaret

"Stop at the corner and let me buy a paper," Clive L......
told the taximan. He was starting to wake up now. What was the Test score, he wondered? The man had only a pile of *Mirrors* and Clive bought one, settling back luxuriously with the tang of a cigarette smarting the raw spot on his tongue. Page One was all Rhodesia and the strike. A headline on Page Two caught his eye and he read the story:

"After strangling his mistress with nylons and green tights, and dumping her body in the sea, it was alleged yesterday, company director Charles T...... answered a 'lonely hearts' advertisement by a woman.

"T......, 50, was said to have told a detective: 'I read an advertisement in a newspaper; "have you got a tiger in your tank and a void in your heart?"

" 'It gave a box number, so I just wrote a letter saying, "I have a tiger in my tank," and she wrote a letter back to me.'

"T...... later met the woman and they spent a day at the seaside, a court also heard.

"And it was said, a fortnight before the nude body of his

36

mistress was washed ashore, the 'lonely hearts' woman—who was not named in court—drove to his flat and spent four days with him."

Hmm, he thought. Fine goings-on. He chuckled and tore the story out of the paper. Angela, who did not take the *Mirror*, would enjoy it when he got back tomorrow night.

He stretched a little wearily. About time he spent an evening at home, now that her mother had at last left them. The thought occupied him until the cab had swung off the Cromwell Road and into the new continental airport terminal building.

At the check-in desk, a tall girl in an expensive looking fur coat and hat was ahead of him. She was standing rather tensely, talking to the uniformed man behind the desk in a low voice. He smelt a waft of deeply disturbing perfume and straightened his tie.

As soon as he had registered his single suitcase he followed her over to the coffee bar and took the stool next to her. She looked up and he smiled.

"Going to Paris?" he asked as casually as possible. She nodded. "So am I. God! What an awful hour to face up to British coffee!"

She smiled, and he liked the evenness of her white teeth against pale lilac lip-tint. But it was not until she spoke that he realized she was French.

"Pleez," she said. "I speak *vairy*-leetle-Eengleesh."

"Don't worry," he told her. "I speak no French at all!"

They both laughed politely.

While they were laughing, at that same moment, 450 miles to the north, a milk-roundsman, muffled in knitted balaclava, his breath puffing ahead in grey-white clouds, saw a bundle wrapped in newspaper lying against the wire fence of the tennis club, put down his wire cage of empty bottles and walked gingerly over to where the battered remains of Evelyn H...... lay in the frosty grass.

He stared for a moment or two, holding the edge of the paper in his gloved hands as if undecided whether to examine further; then turned and ran towards the corner of the road where a phone-box stood, leaving his bottles forgotten on the pavement.

When the Duty Sergeant answered, he told him: "You'd better send a man up here quick. There's a young lass's body on the Tufnell Road side of the tennis club. It looks as though she's been done in. Aye, I'll be here . . ." Then he went back to his bottles and stood, banging his hands together against the cold, shuffling his feet until the car drew up. "What's all this, then?" said the burly young uniformed driver. "Where is she?" Two plain-clothes men with orange-rimmed eyes and chin-stubble disgorged, snapping the car's doors shut. All three walked grimly behind the milkman as he led the way to his find. "There," he said, pointing. "Looks like a young 'un, too. Poor lass." The policemen moved over to the body. One of them came back. "We'll need your statement," he said in a flat, non-committal voice. "When did you find her?"

For all that remained of this dismal hour, the full processes of British law busied themselves with the tragedy of eighteen-year-old Miss H...... and her violent end. She had been strangled with her own olive green mackintosh belt; stabbed—as the pathologist found later—sixteen times in the chest and stomach; and had died about two hours after this assault, from exposure and loss of blood. A more detailed examination showed that she had also been violently raped by someone "with the strength of an animal" as the coroner's court heard later.

The more surprising thing was not her death, which was to be repeated on average once a month throughout this and all future years of the British calendar (in a statistical trend which was spiralling upwards, and had been ever since the passing of the Street Offences Act), but the circumstances of her life. Evelyn H...... was one of the most virtuous girls in the North of England. Nobody could be found to come forward with any hint of a suggestion that she was other than chaste and virginal. At the library where she worked since leaving school her chief and all colleagues vouched for the fact that Evelyn rarely went out except to Church and to attend musical evenings with the town choral society. Her sole hobby was the tennis she played at the club where her body had been found. But even here she was never involved in the small club's social side and kept to herself. Nobody had ever seen her with a boyfriend. She was said, by her best schoolfriend, to have been "shy to the point of terror" of a boy making advances to her.

The mystery was heightened by the pathological findings. At the time of her death, eighteen-year-old Evelyn H...... was three months pregnant and had been having "regular" sexual intercourse. The report concluded: "It is doubtful if she had been a virgin for the past two or more years."

Some women are anglers aiming to catch the mis-cautious by every look; placing themselves in attitudes to allure the vagrant eye. The trifler can scarcely amuse you for an evening. You can learn nothing from her unless it be the folly of a vacant mind. Come away lest you also catch the same disorder...

> "*The Young Man's Companion, or Friendly Adviser*",
> *Edward Turner*

Chapter 5

8 a.m.

COLD COMFORT

The commuter trains, the steamily-cosy morning buses are rolling; and love removes itself to a safe distance. Yet it lingers in the mind, in the half hazed-over memory of the night; in the nostril perhaps. Its spells are only part erased by morning newspapers; swabbed out by hot tea; dismantled and distorted. If it has almost nowhere to go for comfort at this hour, except to the soft arms of *demi-mondaines* (as foreign to Britain as they sound) yet love still exists.

The young man reading the *Daily Telegraph* on a train approaching rain-sodden Deansgate Station is covering a passion as intense as any experienced by the heroes of Colette. Last night he swore to her that if she would not marry him he could not be responsible for his actions. This morning, still numb with the shock of her refusal, he is contemplating suicide, emigration, dramatic gestures and the French Foreign Legion. Even the Vietnam war would be preferable, he thinks, to his wretchedness.

In the draughty house which her family own in Sale, the young lover's adored is pecking at her breakfast, her mother's eye on

40

her. "You were late last night," she is told. "Aye, well, the concert didn't finish early, and there were that many people at Piccadilly queuing. We didn't get on the first one." She sniffed and blew her nose on a small handkerchief. "Anything the matter, then?" asked her mother, pouring. "No, why?" "You look pale, that's all. Is Geoff all right? You haven't been having words again, have you?" "*Tchk!* Really, Mother . . ." "Well, *have* you? I only asked." "Not really. He's just . . . oh, I don't know. I suppose they're all the same. Always on about *marriage*. Blow him! I want some fun before I settle down and give all my health and strength to raising kids."

Her mother, after a long hard look at her sniffing daughter, changes the subject. A wise woman.

Down south, in the vast, never-sleeping "smoke", or capital city of London, there are plenty of Geoffs and girls like the one in Sale. Plenty of anxious mums. Not all of them as wisely, or as needlessly, so. The old Adam is only appearing to take things easy at this hour, not really losing heart. Cupid knows the sun will bring more pulse beats, more vitamins, more energy and more natural attraction. Boys will meet girls, fall for girls, kiss girls and make love to girls at every minute of every hour of every day in the British calendar. And there's nothing exceptional in this except the way it is disguised by the orderly millions going to work; or cleaning houses and doing chores.

Maureen J......, 28, yawned as she pushed her arms into a dressing-gown, her feet into woolly slippers. The bedroom door of the semi-basement flat in Notting Hill Gate she shared with Timothy A......, 39, was closed but she could hear the rattle of the loose pane in the front door as somebody's knuckles hammered the woodwork. "Coming," she called out, clearing her throat.

The postman seemed enormously large in the morning light. His rough jacket bulged over his heavy arms and standing in the well below street level an aureole of filtered sunlight cast him in sharp relief. "Morning," he said. "One to sign for, please."

She took the bulky recorded delivery package and the stub of chewed pencil, shivering slightly in the cold damp of the well. The name written in pencil on the yellow form was "Timothy A...... Esq." "Oh," she said. "Just a mo'. That's not for me."

Tim was asleep. She shook him gently and he opened his eyes.

41

"Something to sign for," she said. "Oh, God, what time is it?"
"Nearly nine I think." "Oh God."

He took the stub of pencil wrong-end first, tried to write his name, reversed it and wrote his name carefully in the space. Then he flopped back onto the green-and-white-striped pillow, dropping the package unopened among the medley of newspapers and magazines on the floor. Maureen carried the form back to the waiting postman, managed a weak smile, shut the door as he clomped back up the steep stone alleyway stairs and went into the kitchen, wrinkling her nose against the overnight smell of stale fish, putrid onion and garlic. She swished the kettle round and lit the gas under it with a wooden match. Automaton gestures picked two cups off hooks, saucers from a dresser shelf and teaspoons from a drawer. Sugar was in front of her, in a carton with its top torn away. She yawned again, loudly, went to the fridge and plucked out a half full bottle of milk. Then she spooned coffee powder into each cup, adding the water as it came to the boil and finishing off with a dollop of sugar in each and a quick topper of milk. She carried the cups deftly back to bed.

"What was it?" she asked. "Mm?" "What was it the postman brought you?" "Don't know." They sipped in silence for a few seconds, then he put his cup down on the bedside table beside the white telephone and, gasping, lent over to pick up the package. The light was enough to read the name printed on the outside. "Oh," he said. "The cruise tickets."

"Hurrah," she said cynically. "Victory."

"Well, it took long enough." He was tearing open the thick brown paper envelope and searching for the accompanying letter. "Here we are . . . 'Dear Mister A. . . . . . ,' . . . so on and so on . . . here we are . . . 'your ticket and that of Miss M. J. . . . . . who, we understand, will be accompanying you . . .' "

He looked at her and they both laughed. Then he examined the pink booklets of tickets. "All in order," he said. "See . . . 'Cabin B.86, Starboard' on both yours *and* mine. Well, I wonder how much agony of conscience that caused them?"

She was picking at a broken finger-nail. "I don't know why they changed their minds," she said. "None of the other companies would even consider it. What a lot of fuss!"

"Mm."

"Did you know the phone engineers were here yesterday?"
"No. Any joy?"

"They looked a bit shifty. The one in charge seemed all right.

42

But he said they weren't usually allowed to have two subscribers on one premises; or something like that. I asked if it would make any difference if we wanted the phones put in different rooms; not on either side of the same double-bed. He didn't seem to know. Anyway, he said they must have agreed to the installation, or he wouldn't have been sent round."

"Splendid. Perhaps the B.B.C. will be able to get in touch with me, then. I must have missed any number of calls."

"Yes. Where are we going tonight?"

"Surprise."

"Tell me. I know. It's that French place you took me to last time."

"No."

"Well. Hope it's somewhere where we won't be asked what we're celebrating. Do you remember last year, and that funny woman you knew in your youth?"

"Darling. Not *everyone* is broad-minded enough to accept that two old livers-in-sin of ten years standing are coy enough to keep up a rather unusual anniversary. What do you expect? A greetings telegram from Buck House? *'My husband and I congratulate you on having lived together since you first went to bed together ten years ago'* . . . Something like that?"

"*That* would be wild!"

"Mm. No doubt. But if you have trouble with the cruise companies, and all those dreary provincial hotels we always seem to be cohabiting in, what *can* you expect from the establishment?"

"Oh, you're always so *right* about everything. I still can't see why there's such a fuss. I suppose I'll have to wear a ring again this year, won't I? When we go down to the Film Festival. And that means that the whole of my hand gets sunburnt except for one tell-tale white band. Which I then have to cover over with sticking plaster so that my 'colleagues' don't guess my dark secret. It's all too bloody absurd."

He took her hand and pressed it. "Is it?" he asked.

She buried her head in his shoulder. "Yes," she said, her voice muffled by pyjamas. "It is. But I wouldn't dream of anything else. Even if . . ."

He was stroking her soft, pale hair tenderly. "Even if Joan died, or I was allowed to divorce her?"

"Yes. Only that won't happen, anyway. She's been in there now for eight and a half years. *We* both know she's completely dotty, poor thing. But that doesn't change the official attitude, does it?"

"They have to be careful, I suppose."

"*Careful!* They're just interested in their own rules for the sake of them. It's not me it hurts, anyway. It's Jimmy. What happens when he leaves that boarding-school of his and has to face *life*? With a father who lives with a woman who isn't even his step-mother?"

"I know. But he's a sensible lad. And he loves you very much."

"I love him. That doesn't stop the tongues. And the stares. And the whispers. And all the soft idiots who get the idea in their heads that what I need is an 'eligible man'. Bah! They keep introducing me to bore after bore. Sometimes I wish I'd gone the whole hog and had that blessed baby."

"It would have complicated things, certainly."

"Well, we've come *some* way, haven't we? I mean, I can go and buy contraceptives openly at Boots, now, in the Earls Court Road. And the cruise lines don't all insist that we take first-class tickets as they used to, do they?"

"True. This is something I come up against time after time in my scripts. I can go just so far with the chemistry. Love is all right. Even rich, demanding, physical love; providing it's leading up to some sort of respectability. That includes the respectable business of adultery. Or having a quickie with a bloke's best-friend's wife. It's when people stop being dramatic about it and start asking the world to accept them as lovers who don't want to marry or settle down, that's when the trouble starts. And of course the cant is inches thick still. How far do you think we'll ever be able to *go*? On television for instance?"

"In the next ten or twelve years, I should have thought you could have shown a couple hard at it; wouldn't you? You're the writer, *you* ought to know."

"I *don't* know. Nor does the Lord Chamberlain. Or the British Board of Film Censors. Or the Archbishop of Canterbury. All they know is that there are some sights and sounds, and stories —and even scents—that could be said, loosely, to make young soldiers masturbate. And they instinctively wrinkle their Proustian noses and say 'away with these baubles'. I suppose they're right. I suppose we are moving closer to the real thing. But we'll have to get further than a couple grunting and writhing on a London bomb-site, or that shadow-boxing lark in *Dolce Vita*."

"All right. So where does all this get *us*? I don't want to scrub all the cant off the screen and T.V. That doesn't interest me. What I want is a bit more common sense in our daily lives. For God's sake, Ma Grundy was supposed to have died of starvation of her filthy mind years ago. Did you know that in the early part of the war they had to make it official that 'unmarried wives' were to be treated the same as married ones? They gave them the same allowances. And for all I know the unwed widows among them *still* collect pensions."

"Damn it all. Living together isn't a communicable disease like gonorrhæa or syphilis. It's a fact of existence. People do it. If the marriage and divorce laws are too strict, then they do it out of necessity. If the conventions won't allow them their independence, they take it. What's so desperately wrong? We admit we're a pagan country with the emptiest churches in the Christian world. Yet we snap and snarl at any couple wanting to license their own sort of pattern of living outside the humbug of 'holy vows'." She threw herself back on the pillows. "Oh. You know what I think."

"Yes," he said, leaning over to kiss her. "I'm beginning to. What about some breakfast?"

". . . What are they doing to sex, anyway? If these writers insist on bringing everything into the open, even the blood sweat and queers; (and there just cannot be that much blood and sweat) there soon will not be anything left to become excited about. The current literary striptease has destroyed the power and pleasure of the imaination . . ."
Extract from "Writers Newsletter", November 1965

It's about three in the morning. The sky is navy-blue. We walk across a chaos of grass and rubble to a row of deserted houses . . . He strikes a match and looks through a broken window. "Comin' in?" Strewn over the torn-up wooden boards lie a bicycle wheel, two mattresses and a pair of National Health glasses. We go upstairs. There are just two rooms, one off each side. "When I saw yer sittin' there I began to sizzle: 'I'm in it tonight,' I thought . . . 'let's sit down. You smell as if you never sweated in yer life . . .' " He spreads his coat over the bare boards . . . The smell of damp from the mattress against my cheek . . . At five in the morning a bird sang a complicated song. "That's a thrush," he says. "I don't love my wife because I wasn't her first—she went with another bloke when she was sixteen." He combs his hair and I look at the early sun dappling the filth.
"Up the Junction", Nell Dunn (MacGibbon & Kee)

So, at eight—or anyway before nine—in the morning we have established the fact that illicit love in liberal, emancipated Britain of the sixties is easier than respectable sin. Who is surprised, or even disturbed? Has all the stern moralizing of the Sunday newspapers been in vain? All the punctilious and public-spirited collation of statistics? *"Did you know that in this country seventy marriages end in divorce every day? That of all first babies born one in three is conceived before the parents marry?"* Of course you didn't, or the paper would not have been hammering it into you as an excuse for running a *"Don't Miss This!"* series of articles ("... startling facts ... disturbing ... making a mockery of marriage ... will shock millions") *investigating* the situation. Well, "dig and you allus find worms", as the old fisherman said. There's plenty not too sweet-smelling about our island behaviour patterns. Especially in the realms of Venus and Eros and Cupid and company. *Cruelty for instance ...*

Dr Julian de S...... did not knock. He came into his wife's bedroom almost boisterously. There was a busy, purposeful air about him, from the thin pleating of wrinkles on his smooth, tall brow to the perfect mirror of his glacé toe-caps.

"Vivienne," he called softly into the gloom cast by the heavy velvet curtains. "My sweetheart, it's well past eight; and you know what morning this is, my love?"

Vivienne de S...... lay in the centre of the room surrounded by well-polished furniture. At first glance, her bed looked as though it were an operating table, or mobile stretcher. Then it could be seen that it was a clinical couch; though not an ordinary model. This was an expensive, well-padded affair with beautifully tooled, stainless-steel adjustments and the most splendid foam rubber upholstery under the rich leather which provided the outer surface of its length. Vivienne lay asleep and fully relaxed on it, her reddish hair like wire wool against the anaemic cleanliness of the sheets and bedding. Her eyes, green and dark-fringed, opened wide the moment her husband spoke.

"I'll be ready," she said dully. "I'm getting up now."

He had moved to the foot of her bed and was fussing over cushions on a long timber and woven-cane settee. "Excellent," he said. "I simply can't dream of being late for the Countess at 10.30. God knows what would happen!"

She was sitting up, clumsily drawing a faded négligé of pink artificial silk over her plump, freckled arms and shoulders. "I'll ... I'll be as quick as I can," she said.

He went to the window and drew back the curtain, looking down into Wimpole Street and seeing the wet, black cars go hissing along the shiny length of it. Pale sunshine was slanting into the opposite houses, but the street was in shadow. "I hope she doesn't come by car," he said. "The last time ... remember?

She said she'd been going round in circles for three-quarters of an hour before she found a free meter."

His wife yawned; at the same time she covered her hand with a fluttering, affected gesture. "She ought to walk, I should think," she said tartly. "The exercise would do her good."

He looked at her, frowning. "She's a terribly sick person, my love."

"My foot!"

"I suppose you wouldn't pay any attention to her reiterated threat to kill herself? If you were me, I mean? Her analyst?"

"My dear Jubu, *if* I were you I would not in the first instance dream of *being* her analyst. For me, the Contessa Leonia Elizabetta Gronchi-Faranto is one big, disgusting fraud. She makes me sick!"

He looked at his watch with a nervously impatient gesture. "Well, never mind," he said. "She will be here quite soon, and I *do not wish* a repetition of last Tuesday morning to occur; you understand, Vivienne?"

"Oh, I'll take myself off. For goodness sake let me have time to wake up and remove the offending evidence of my presence from your *magnificent* consulting room. From your *superb* couch; where only your best and most suicidal patients may lay their fair bodies by day. And where your wife—your own wife—has to try to rest at night. No, don't worry about me. I'll be gone without trace in just a moment."

She was on her feet, collecting garments and bedding in a huge roll which she clasped to her rotund frame. Anger had pinkened her cheeks. Her eyes were unnaturally bright. He looked at her with distaste.

"There is absolutely no need," he said with controlled vehemence, "for you to sleep here at all. It is *your* idea, I think you will remember that, won't you? Wasn't it *you* who insisted that I occupy the bedroom upstairs, so that I could rest after the work I must now do. Did you not tell me it was taking too great a toll of me? Was that not the reason for this whole . . ." he paused, then ejected the final word with contempt ". . . *charade!*"

She sighed in a tremulous, frustrated and nervous fashion. "Oh, I *suppose* you're right," she said. "You *do* have to work far too hard. And you must get your sleep. But all this analysis . . . oh, Jubu, do you really have to do so much of it? Couldn't we just go back to medicine and forget about Freud? *Couldn't* we, my precious?"

He was tidying papers at the neat, polished, mahogany desk.

"Please, Vivienne," he said, as though to a fractious child. "You know I must continue with the work. How would the patients manage if I broke off now?"

For a moment, in the process of opening the door leading to the bathroom, she paused rebelliously. Then she shrugged. "I suppose so," she said. "Well, I'll be out in a moment and you won't see me again to bother your dear patients for the rest of the day. I suppose you're not in to lunch? No, of course not. Well, *auf Wiedersehen*. Till tonight."

He straightened up from the desk, frowning. Something was held between his finger and thumb. "And Vivienne," he called shrilly. "*Please* don't leave your hair grips on the desk. You *know* how upsetting it is when the patients see them."

She was halfway through the door, carrying her bedding. She did not reply. When she closed the door, it shut firmly, almost with a bang.

It is generally accepted in analysis that moral codes testify not only to the cultural environment, but also to the personality of the individual who holds them . . .

Analysis is as little a never-failing key to morality as it is, as Freud was the first to realise, a reliable key to happiness . . .

For us, analysis is primarily a therapeutic and not a moral instrument.
    "Psychoanalysis and Moral Values," Heinz Hartmann, M.D.

Chapter 6

9 a.m.

SWITCHED ON

There are times of day when love is in retirement; this is one of them. But if Cupid rests at this baleful hour, his work goes on. The pulses and fantasies and memories, the teeth-marks of the love bites, are all still there. They are secreted behind make-up; hidden under clothing and sober expressions; submerged by factory whistles; the clickety-clack of typewriters and the rustle of invoices; papers and ledger leaves. But they are still there. What has happened is that a huge, universal switch has been pushed over to the "on" position, and the buzz and hum and rattle of a working day has jumped to life behind a screen of noise. It is only a mask. Underneath, love goes on. And on.

Margie B...... had eaten a small plate of crispened rice cereal and drunk half a cup of tea for her breakfast, but her mother was still worried about her. "What is it, Margie dear?" she asked. "You're not poorly, are you? Do you think you ought to stay home from school today?"

The girl insisted she was all right. She took her satchel and her mack, wrapped the blue and yellow scarf of Marketon High School round her throat and went out to catch the Blue Bus. As she walked up Finucane Street, past the piles of steaming manure and hay from Captain Grindle's riding stables, her pace became increasingly sluggish. She was still several yards from the small knot of people waiting under the oak tree at the corner when the bus pulled up.

After everyone had got in, it seemed as if the bus would start away without her; but Fred, the driver, must have glimpsed her in his mirror as she trotted up. He pushed open the hinged, manually-operated door and watched her climb aboard. "Buck up, Margie," he said amiably. "Don't keep us all waiting, now." She managed a quick, fleeting smile and moved, head high, to the first vacant seat only two rows back.

The bumpy ride was uneventful. She was unconscious of cold. All her thoughts were on the unfinished homework in her satchel; on what Miss Evans would say. She was frightened. Last time she had been warned not to overlook it again. Now she had to expect the worst. All last evening she had wasted time in front of the television. Not really watching the programmes but using them as a screen to hide her feelings at the thought of the baby inside her. By the time she had come to it, the work had seemed tasteless and impossibly hard. She had only done a sketchy job, then tumbled into bed.

The bus swayed and bumped along the narrow road. In under ten minutes, as was usual when there was no fog, mist, ice, snow or flooding, they were approaching Marketon railway station. She held fourpence ready in her gloved hand and she paid it on her way out, smiling again. Fred took the money, punched a ticket and threw it into a heap beside him. "Ta-ta," he said. Margie climbed down the steps, feeling her stomach tauten under her tight-waisted, grey, school skirt.

Abruptly it came to her that she would not go to school this morning. She had no plan, no clear idea of how long she would stay away; or what she would do with her time. But as soon as the thought formed in her mind she felt relieved; as though a great, crushing weight had rolled away. It was exciting.

She had twelve shillings and ninepence in her suede purse, ten shillings of it saved from her auntie's present when she had come to see them. It was enough to take her to Salisbury. This much she knew, because she had been several times with her mother; and twice with Ron. In the back of her mind was a faint, un-spoken hope that a coffee-bar he had taken her to might offer the sort of sanctuary she craved at this moment. At all events it was warm, friendly and timeless.

"Salisbury, please," she said to the man in the ticket office. He looked up, curious. "Single or return?" he asked. "Oh, single," she said, suddenly breathless. "Somebody's bringing me back by car."

In fact, she was afraid that too much of her money would go on the fare. She would need all she had. Coffee in the coffee-bar, as she remembered, was a whole shilling. Anyway, she couldn't just sit in a bar all day.

He punched the ticket and passed it to her. "Not going to school today, then?" he asked. "That's right," she said. Again she managed a smile, as she had on the bus. "I've got the day off." "Enjoy yourself," he said. He smiled suggestively and she turned away.

The train was practically empty. She chose a non-smoker with nobody at all inside. Through the steamy windows its electric lighting looked cosy and attractive. As she sank into a corner seat, she felt a rush of terror at what she was doing, and an instantaneous return of the flood of relief she had felt earlier. Somewhere in her, the dumb misery of her plight was at last weeping openly.

As she thought of it, her eyes filled. She was crying quietly, hunched low with the pain, when the whistle blew. She felt the coach give a lurch. There was a shout from the guard on the station, a man's figure appeared running, her door wrenched open and he flung himself aboard. She sat up, blowing her nose.

"Phew!" he said. "That was close." He laughed, and slammed the door behind him. Then he threw himself, panting onto the opposite seat. After a minute, she dared to look across at him.

He was about forty, dressed in tweeds and wearing brown leather boots. He had no hat and his black, strong hair was brushed and oiled tight against his skull. He was very dark, but not unfriendly. She took all this in at a glance.

"Going up to Salisbury?" he asked her.

"Yes."

"Ah. You'll be there in good time on this. Fast one, isn't it?"

She nodded, wondering if her eyes were red-rimmed from the bout of weeping. She had no idea about the train but did not like to expose her ignorance.

"Just as well, too," he said. "If I'm not at the hospital by ten-thirty there'll be trouble."

51

There was silence for a moment. Then she ventured to reply. "Are you ill, then?" she asked.

"No, no," he said. "I'm a doctor."

More of the upper class (88 per cent) than of the lower class (81 per cent) think that men and women should get enjoyment out of sexual relations. Conversely, more of the lower class (9 per cent) than of the upper class (7 per cent) think men and women should have sex relations only for the purpose of having children.

From "Television and Religion",
a report prepared by Social Surveys (Gallup Poll)
Ltd. on behalf of ABC Television

Quintessentially, the Duke of S...... was telling his daughter Merilyn as they drove towards Hawkchallis, one must try to remember at all moments of embarrassment that one is *in the right*. "Your mother," he said with something of the pitying weariness which, in the war, the German puppet broadcaster Joyce had reserved for British ministers, "is behaving extremely badly over this whole thing. She is forcing our hand."

The Hon. Merilyn, a thickly-made young woman of 23, was chain-smoking cheap cigarettes and driving the shooting brake at the same time. She laughed. "It sounds like a game of polo," she said. "Or a battle."

Her father was silent. "I just hope the damn gardeners aren't about yet," he said. "Nobody else will be. And your mother is sure to be asleep. She hasn't opened her eyes before noon for ten years."

They drove through the gates and a lace curtain, none too clean, stirred in a window of the stone-faced lodge. "Old Mrs Cheedle," said the Duke. "Sees everything; but she hasn't a telephone; and her gout's too bad to let her get about. You could march the whole British Army up here if you wanted to."

"She's a disgusting old woman," said Merilyn. "Keeps millions of cats."

A drive of over a half a mile brought them under the mossy, stone battlements of the old house. It was gargantuan rather than grand. The Duke got out and approached the enormous, studded, oak front door. "Come along," he told his daughter. "I've still got my key."

They passed inside. Suits of armour gleamed at them in the shaded hall. A large golden dog, asleep on a woman's fur coat in front of a freshly lit fire, got up, sniffed and came ambling towards them, wagging its tail. "Hallo, Bastard," said the Duke, patting the dog's head. "How're the worms?"

The dog growled appreciatively, then turned and settled back on its soft couch, yawning. The Duke's hand-made shoes creaked on the old timbering of the stairs as they took them two at a time. From somewhere deep inside the house came the sounds of preparation for the day; it was muffled and incurious. Nobody came to disturb the intruders.

Upstairs, the gallery leading to the main bedrooms was luxuriously carpeted from panelling to panelling; their tread was muffled. An old, iron, ring-latch on the Duchess's door squeaked as the Duke turned it. Then they were inside.

Myra, seventh Duchess of S......, lay in an almost foetal position in the low double-bed; backed by pink-tinted mirrors. The whole room was pink. Against it her auburn hair seemed immensely dark. A white cairn terrier lay fast asleep in a corner of the heavy ivory satin eiderdown which had slipped from the bed. The room was warm; heavy with perfume.

"Sssh!" breathed the Duke. "You stand here. No need to come further. Just want a witness, that's all."

He tiptoed towards the bed, looked dispassionately at the sleeping form of his wife, opened a small lacquered drawer in a bedside table and took out a red, leather-covered diary. Two minutes later they were back in the car. A man in shirt sleeves popped his unshaven head out of the front door as Merilyn started the motor. He saw the Duke and half-grinned, sheepishly. Then he went back inside.

For the length of the drive, they rode in silence. Then the Duke said, "Thanks, darling." He took out a slim gold case and opened it with an elegant sliding gesture. "Time for a cigarette, eh?" She stubbed out her half-finished butt and accepted a flat Egyptian from her father. He lit it and then his own. "Ah," he said with satisfaction. "Now we'll see what Her Ladyship has to say about things." He tapped his pocket. "I almost tremble to think what indiscretions we shall find in here."

Merilyn winced slightly. "Oh, dear," she said. "I do so wish all this wasn't necessary, Daddy. It seems too beastly for words."

"What? Nonsense. It's the law, my dear. Must have evidence. Just because you and I both know about your mother's incessant peccadilloes, that doesn't mean a damn thing to a judge. He wants *proof*—right—well, now we've got it."

She changed down. "How do you know? You haven't read it

yet. I don't think Mummy would be so silly as to put anything down . . ."

He interrupted: "Of course she did! That's the whole, incredible thing. She has a perfect *mania* for confiding her secrets to herself; don't you know that?"

"No, I do not."

"What about all those letters to you when you were at the finishing place in Switzerland? Eh? Do you suppose she bothered to go into such incredible detail about my 'cruelty', as she put it, merely for your innocent eyes?"

"Well . . . yes. At least I'd always imagined they were for me. If not, then who else?"

"For *herself*, of course. She kept copies of them all. I know. I've seen them in her desk, filed away in neat, little bundles. Oh, she's got the mind of an estate manager's clerk, that woman."

"Daddy, please. She *is* my mother."

"Hmm. And I'm your father." The Duke lowered the window and threw out his cigarette. "At least, so I have always fondly believed, my dear; in spite of everything your mother has since done to sow the seeds of doubt in my mind."

She offered no reply. The Hon. Merilyn was wondering in the depths of her rather secretive mind whether this was the ideal opportunity she had been seeking for several past weeks to tell her father about her engagement. To Abdul Ali Ben Mustapha K......, studying phrenology with her in South Kensington. She decided that it was. "Daddy . . ." she began.

With his helmet off, the sergeant had a wry face. There was no certainty that he was smiling, but the impression was there. In the wrinkles at the corner of his small, pale eyes; and in the folds of white, freckled skin round his thin mouth. "What's this then," he was saying to Fred F...... in the little cell down at Tatford Road Police Station, "Assault and . . ." He pursed his thin lips. "I see. Well, you're in a nice old mess and no mistake, aren't ye, lad?"

Fred sat on the small, wooden wall-seat, his head between his knees, looking at the floor between twitching hands. It kept repeating itself in his tired brain, over and over again; nothing he could do would shut it out. *What will our ma say when she gets t'know?*"

He was hardly conscious of the sergeant. None of them mattered. He had put up no resistance at all after Alice M...... had screamed; just gone along with the two puffing constables who had come to the house and up the stairs in answer to her and the neighbours' yells. They'd handled him roughly at first; but when they'd got him downstairs and into the car, it was obvious he hadn't any fight left in him. At the station they almost ignored him; after taking down the particulars, that was.

For half an hour or more he'd been sitting here, now. Since putting his clothes back on properly. They had brought these with them, only making him wrap his nude body in his mack. They they'd thrown them in after him. He found he was short of one sock. The money and wallet had gone out of his pockets. He just put his shoes on and tied them over his bare foot.

"Well, lad," the sergeant was saying. "I've come to see if I c'n help thee, like. Nothing's so bad as it seems, y'know, provided you use a bit of what you've got up here." He tapped his close-cropped ginger head like a seductive schoolmaster. "See, son? I know how you're feeling now. But why not make a nice clean breast of everything—with me to help you—and I guarantee, lad, you'll feel a heap better straight away. What about it, eh? Here's the form. All very plain and straightforward. Just tell me what you want to write and we'll put it all down like you say; eh, son?"

Fred pulled himself together and faced the visitor. "What is it?" he asked. "A statement? Yes, I suppose I might as well. What's the bloody use of it now, though?"

"Aye, well, you mustn't feel like that. Not a bit of good. Now, let me see . . ." the sergeant put the buff form on the table and produced a ball-point pen from his tunic pocket. "Here we are . . . We can leave the details: name, age and such like. We've got those booked in the office. Now, what happened before our lads brought you in? Just put it simply, in your own words, son. And don't talk too quickly, now, because I want to get it all down right, see? Go on."

Fred hesitated. He cleared his throat. "I went to the house," he said. "I had the key, see. Well, there's nothing to it. I went upstairs and into the room. I don't know what came over me. It was daft, bloody daft. But that's what I did and that's why I'm here. What else do you want to know?"

So far, the sergeant had not written anything down. He was studying Fred with a new interest. "This'll be Mrs M . . . . . . , will it?" he asked. Fred nodded. "A nice bit of stuff, that. But what on earth possessed you . . . ah, well, we all do silly things from time to time, I suppose. All right, just let me put that down. 'I . . . had . . . a . . . . key . . . to . . . Mrs . . . M . . . . . . 's . . .

55

house ... and gained ... entry ... without her or anybody else's ... consent. I climbed ... the stairs ... and entered ... the room ... where ... Mrs M.......... was asleep ... Then ... I ... took ... off ... all ... my ... clothes ... and ... got ... into ... bed ... beside Mrs M.......... ." He looked up. "And got what you'd come for, eh?"

"Me? I didn't bloody touch her."

"Oh, come now, lad. Who's going to believe that of a game chap like you? Better cough it all up now, take my word."

"I didn't touch her. She ... I thought ... well, when she turned, and saw I weren't her husband, Joe, she fair bellowed. I had to hide in the bloody wardrobe to get away from her. I think she'd a' killed me if she could a' found anything sharp or heavy enough even."

"Aye. And that's *all* that happened, is it?" The sergeant was plainly disappointed. "Are you really sure you didn't slip her one, like, while she was still half asleep?"

"What do you bloody well think? If she'd o' let me, I wouldn't be here now, would I?"

"What*ever* made tha' do it, lad?"

"I *tell* you, I was a bloody mug! Read too many cheap books, I suppose. I don't know. Make up your own reasons. What'll I get for this lot, any road?"

"It's a sight too early to be bothering your head about things like that yet, lad. Just keep calm. And now perhaps you'll read this statement and sign at the bottom there. Then we'll have to see about getting you some breakfast. Have you had tea yet? No, well leave it to me."

He took the form, appraised the signature, got up and went to the door, taking a key out of his pocket and opening it on the inside. "By the way," he said, turning, "we've let your ma know. One of our lads is calling on her now. I expect she'll be down to see you directly. She can bring your things, can't she?" He let himself out, slamming the door and locking it from the outside.

Numbly, the young man heard him go. Inside, there was a wobbling jelly that had been Frederick F...... "Bloody 'ell," he thought. "This is a right bloody mess I'm in this time. How can I face her?"

Chapter 7

10 a.m.

I SAY, I SAY

The birds and the bees are still at it, no doubt; but at this po-faced, practical hour the rest of civilized man- and womankind accepts a moratorium on physical love. It is driven underground: into the post-operative wards of hospitals where the Old Adam, revived by tea and sympathy, is breaking through the bandages and leering out of the neatly tucked-in hospital corners of the beds. A nurse's hand on a pulse . . . a thermometered finger brushing an unshaven lip . . . the look that passes between "have you?" and the requisite reply . . . these are occasions for a furtive quantity of loving.

Across the littered trays and typewriters of the large offices, eyes meet and tangle. In factory canteens, shops and even on the windy platforms of corporation buses, Cupid's hardier version wings home a few honeyed darts. I'm not denying that the whole works are still banging ahead somewhere, in a rabelaisian, night-into-day world; and certainly the good ladies of outer Soho and Blackpool's Golden Mile are as likely to be flat on their backs earning an honest crust as ever. But ten is not an hour which first-features romance with a capital R.

More a time for mental experiment. For tasting memories and allowing fantasy its head. A time to hold back on the lust which bodies know without respect for time or place. To halt awhile; and to sniff the wind.

Teenage students are discussing sex education into microphones for a T.V. programme. A boy says: "Well, I think the best way to be taught is . . . not to be taught. Just to learn to accept it. From when you're very young, so that it never has to be brought up in a conversation."

A girl: "We had some primitive sex education when we were about 11, during our first year at grammar school. The teacher sort-of sneaked up to her target through amoeba and spirogyra and bunnies and pussies; and everybody was thinking 'oh, that'll be nice, when we get to it.' And then—quick—human reproduction . . . straight through and back on to something else."

A boy: "Well, my experience is very similar to yours. We were on the flowering plant. And then the next week they suddenly came up with reproduction in rabbits. A week after that we had reproduction in humans. And then they went back on the flowering plant again."

Another boy: "I found that in some biology lessons I simply couldn't understand the words. You know, big ones. It might be just me, I don't know . . ."

Girl: "We had rather a quaint discussion in the first year about worms, and then we had nothing else until the fourth year, which was at the age of fifteen; straight into sexual talk, with marriage-guidance women; and this made you rather embarrassed towards the questions, because you thought you knew most of it . . ."

Another girl, butting in: "Did you have more than one talk on sex?"

Original girl: "No, we only had one."

Second girl: "Yes, well we had this sort of primitive one when we were eleven or twelve. And then we had another quite good one when we were fifteen. And the biology mistress absolutely *rolled* in it. She *loved* it. And it really was quite good, and it taught us *some* things; but most of it we knew already and we just sort of sat and sniggered."

Boy: "Don't you think it's so much better, instead of having formal sex education, just to be told things, from an early age?"

Girl: "Yes, I do. I think perhaps you should tell your children as soon as they ask things. I think it's childish to just sort of say —you know . . . It's most frustrating when somebody says to you: 'there's *something* I'm going to tell you when you're a bit older.' "

Boy: "And when you're older, it's probably too late. You probably know it already. So it doesn't matter."

Another boy: "I disagree. *Do* you think you know it already? *I* don't think I know all about sex, even now . . ."

Boy: "No."

Other boy: ". . . I keep finding out things."

Boy: "I had about three or four discussions with my mother. On sex education. And all she was doing in effect was just telling me what I'd already heard from other sources."

Other boy: "Yes. But suppose the sources are wrong, and you want to be correct. And you're scared to ask. That's the thing, isn't it?"

Girl: "Mmm, yes. That *is* the thing. You're embarrassed, aren't you?"

Boy: "Yes, yes. Yes. Because you hear jokes, and they might be all the other way round. And, and you *think* you know it, but you're scared to ask; because you *think* you know it, sort of thing."

Girl: "Yes. You sort of hear something, and then a biology teacher will tell you something *slightly* different; and you don't want to look silly, do you?"

Boy: "No, that's right; *yeah.*"

Other boy: "It *must* be taught, in a way, by teachers who know about the subject; and not like subjects like Scripture— where the P.E. master comes in and teaches you Scripture in his off-period, while he's resting from the gymnasium. He doesn't know anything about Scripture so he reads football books, or something like that . . ."

Girl: "I only part agree with that, Peter; because it's—sort of like you ask the biology mistress . . . and you're making sex detached again. I mean, you get sex cropping up all over the place. In Literature, and in Scripture. And if all the teachers are *frank*, it just becomes a sort of part of the wildly-gay round . . ."

Other girl: "I think your *parents* should bring it up with you when you're younger. And so it's with you all the time, and you've learnt from scratch, and you just accept it. And it's just an accepted thing."

Boy: "Yes, I agree with that . . ."

Other boy: "Well, I *agree* with it; but I don't think it'll work, because parents get to get embarrassed. And I don't think that parents, well, *know* all about sex themselves (*stifles laugh*) . . ."

Girl: "When I sort of started taking an interest, I asked my mother where babies came from, and she said—quite reasonably —that they came from God. So I sort of had a vision of a baby sort of materializing out of thin air . . ."

Boy: "From a stork?"

Girl: "Yes! And I wanted like anything to be a nurse, so I could see which end God began with . . . the foot or the head!" (*Laughter.*)

Girl: "I first had, mm, my experience with dirty jokes. At school. And, mm, then it sort of straightened itself out in the end; and then anything I wanted to know I went to my mother. And asked. And she told me quite freely; anything I wanted to know."

Boy: "Yes, I think that an accumulation of dirty jokes— although one, or two, or even three of them, may be inaccurate— on the whole, I think you get a sort of rough picture of what's happening. I mean, you get a sort of vague outline of the story, and by piecing them all together you can build up something which is fairly accurate."

Girl: "The only trouble with dirty jokes is, and learning that way is, it does make sex something terribly *detached*. And *sordid*."

Other girl: "Yes."

Girl: "You don't get any idea of the *emotion*."

Boy: "It's not only through sort of animals; and dirty jokes; that you get an idea of sex being sordid. I think that parents, sort of, make it *more* sordid by keeping it dark all the time, don't you think?"

Girl: "It's just the sheer fact they won't discuss it, isn't it?"

Boy: "It's all something hidden. And this must come back from the Victorian times . . . sort of hide things away."

Girl: "The thing is that—if you've got all your, sort of, academic knowledge more or less off pat . . . and then you suddenly do start to react . . . the way you've been told you will. It's absolutely *terrifying*!"

Boy: (laughing) "Yeah."

Girl: (giggling) "It is!"

Boy: "Of course. As most, I think, the majority of boys go to schools which are all boys, and the majority of girls go to schools which are all girls, when they actually meet this is a *big* event."

Unanimous chorus: "Yeah . . ."

Of all the adolescents in this country, only about a quarter—one in four—ever get any factual sex education from their parents at all. And not all of these will get much more than a talk about the birds and the bees.

The one who comes out worst out of these is the working-class boy. He's the one who's least likely to receive sex education at school and is also the one who is least likely to get any help from his parents.

"The Sexual Behaviour of Young People",
Michael Schofield

Afterwards, Margie could never remember exactly how it was she first came to talk about her baby, or what made her do it. He had nice eyes. And he wasn't like most of the other men, and boys, she knew. Perhaps it was his education. There was something soft, yet strongly-bedded, in him which gave her a feeling of warmth and encouragement. She needed to tell somebody, of course. And his being a doctor may have opened the latch on her mental gate.

Whatever it was, as the train swayed them both along towards Salisbury, she began to exchange confidences with this stranger who had chosen her compartment to jump into as the train was pulling out; directed there either by fate or wild chance, whichever way you choose to look at it. He listened carefully, but made none of the shocked faces she would have expected.

Indeed, Dr Ian F...... (he told her his name when he gave her his professional card, before they parted) was a most sympathetic listener. He appeared familiar with all these matters, as though it was quite an everyday thing for a twelve-year-old schoolgirl to conceive a child after only one—her first—sexual encounter. Also, he seemed to understand exactly how she felt, and how distressing, indeed well-nigh impossible, it was for her to go to school. Hence her present flight.

He not only listened, he finally offered some strange but exciting advice. "Don't worry about a thing," he told her. "You must find a way of getting to London to see a friend of mine. Whether or not you tell your mother is neither here nor there at the moment. But you must get up to town, fairly soon. Do you know any way you can do that?"

She didn't.

"Then leave it to me," he told her. "I will be in touch with you as soon as I possibly can. By the way, this friend of mine is not a doctor, exactly. He's a medical analyst. His job is to see that you are mentally prepared to meet this situation."

"What'll I have to pay him?" she asked innocently.

"Nothing at all, my dear. Just show him this card—" it was then that he handed over one of his visiting cards, taken from the top right-hand pocket of his waistcoat "—and I'll let him know you are coming. Will you do that, when I ask you to?"

"Yes, I'll try. I mean; if I can, I will."

"Good. Now. Don't worry about your baby. Don't worry about a thing. It's a good thing we met, because I can help you. You're going to let me, aren't you?"

"Yes."

"Good girl."

She felt his eyes on her bare, stockingless legs and pulled down her gym-slip skirt with an awkward gesture.

Fred F...... sipped his tea and watched while the sergeant wrote it all down. Again. This was the third go they'd had at getting a statement from him. Each time they'd come back in and said something about it not being right, or something. He couldn't make it out. His mind was confused and aching, numb from tiredness and shock. His inside quaked whenever he thought of his mother, and the constable telling her about his crime. She'd be washing up the breakfast things after his dad, or perhaps already going over the hallway stair carpet with the vacuum cleaner. She probably wouldn't believe the policeman at first. Not about her Fred, she wouldn't. Not about him assaulting, or molesting, or whatever they'd call it, Alice. She knew Alice and her husband. She wouldn't believe Fred would get mixed up with her in that way unless he was daft. Well, he *was* bloody daft, wasn't he?

Mrs F...... came in so quietly about 10.50 that he hardly noticed her. She was sitting beside him in a minute, still breathing heavily from the trudge up the slight slope past the gasworks and towards the station. She had his small attaché case—the one he used on weekends, potholing—and her apron, her working apron, folded into a tight roll in the other hand. She must have picked it up in the house, he surmised; so put out by all that was passing through her mind that she had forgotten to put it down. She must have come all the way, on the bus and all, with it.

"Freddie," she said. "What've you gone and done?"

62

Her voice was lower, more mournful and somehow resonant than he had ever heard it. He felt a start of surprise at the change in her. Her eyes, always dark but now seemingly black and enlarged, said more to him than her words. The rebuke, the agony, and the solid acceptance of his sin as hers—*of* her, *by* and *from* her—were clearly expressed in her gaze. He saw and understood. *So this was how a mother felt.* In the instant of realization, he tore inwardly. Everything boyish in him perished and he was an ageless, ever-sinning man. He *was* Man, in all his blackness. The woman before him was his judge and maker.

"Don't worry, Mum," he told her. "I'm O.K."

She looked at him for a long, dry, awful minute. Then she said: "You'll want your things."

"Yes."

Do we need this reminder that the romantic caprice of Fred F...... was bound to bring disaster? Perhaps so. In the parks and public places where certain mentally misshapen men, somewhat incredibly, expose their sexual parts to women of all ages, attractions and classes, there is a vast question mark hanging over such activities as Fred F...... has got up to. It is *why*? Why do they do it?

At a dance, the sailor's face was still stinging from her slap when the outraged girl he had asked to sleep with him said: "Surely you don't say that to *all* girls you dance with?" "Oh, yes I do," said the sailor. "You must," she said, "get an awful lot of smacks in the face." He laughed. "Yes," he admitted, "But I get a lot of girls to sleep with me as well."

Clive L...... was dodging the traffic in Paris. He was on his way to a meeting, with his firm's French colleagues. He was delighted, as only an Englishman in Paris on what was promising to be a rather lovely, even heady, day, can be when he has set himself up for the hours ahead.

For Clive, the hours would be unable to circulate fast enough until 8 p.m., when he had arranged, during shared drinks on the plane, to meet Yvette, the tall, fur-coated French girl. Fortunately, he lacked the ability to see her at this moment.

She sat in the features room of *Elle*. Her long, blonde hair was masking a very English face (she had been born and bred in Minehead) almost as completely as a yashmak. Her eyes, slitting through the double tramlines of heavy black mascara, sparkled

with glee. "Told him, darling, one's name was Yvette . . . 'plees
. . . no speek mooch Eengleesh'. And, darling, he bought, but
the whole bit! One is dining with him—I mean 'veez heem'—
ce soir. C'est amusant, non?"

C'est amusant, si.

Chapter 8

11 a.m.

GO, LOVELY ROSE

At last, recovery is at hand. Warmth and the sweat of work dissolve the crystals of morning, letting the blood flow and the mind relax into dreams. These are not the involuntary masques of night, where a man has so little control he may find himself forced into intimacy with partners too awful to imagine on waking. They are wish-blown, halcyon, spun of need and vision ... dreams with a purpose which will come about, or rust a man's inner self. Do the women dream? Not of such things. Of love, while playing with the tides of sex, no doubt; but not of sex, of the warm spring of physical love, toying only with the false swell of love. For such deceit, look into the mind of man about 11 of the clock on any English morn. Do not be shocked by what you see and smell there. Love is a splendidly disgusting pattern; at the design stage, that is. Though some would deny its existence.

Miss Janet Suzman was barely at ease in the comfortable armchair. In spite of the music, soft and classical, pouring like a breeze fed on spring flowers through the morning room of her South African parents' flat in Kensington, London. A nice room. A more than pretty girl. Something there, in the firm, boyish set of the head on the strong young neck. Something that has attracted critics and connoisseurs, and more momentously the two experienced eyes of Mr Peter Hall, casting and casting about for actresses who could act with their bodies, their breathing, their very souls and selves rather than just via lines however brilliant. In her, he found a Maid of Orleans still vibrating in a million tele-memories; an actress of stature. Not yet vain or distant; but of this earth, earthy without the least vulgarity. A sound and useful person, given to thought and the reservation of judgement; opposed to empty generality. A woman in many, and one who came to Britain from abroad, hence saw us with a naked eye. Yet called us "us" and talked of "we".

"Most people have their own traffic-light system," she said quietly. "I don't really think we are very different from other nationalities. The French, perhaps, and the Americans are more puritanical. Morally, who can say one outruns the other? There are extremists of every kind; and not only of sex."

A pause. Miss Suzman is thinking about the British *as lovers*. Her expression suggests that the thought is not displeasing. "But as lovers of what?" she inquired with a twinkle, "dogs, cricket, cars, wine, women, Sundays? Oh, all right, women it is!"

Another pause. The same look of pleasant reminiscence: "I lived in Florence for three months once," she said, "when I'd just left school. The Italians are charming, because they expect failure. They shrug and smile winningly if their advances are repulsed. But they will try anything on. The only time I have ever smacked a man's face was in Italy. It hurt me more than it hurt him, I think."

A small smile of apology. Then: "That was my first and my last face slap. I did it for purely literary reasons. To see what would happen. I must have been reading very bad books at the time. Now, happily, I find that I can manage without resorting to such extremes."

About the English, though? What about our reputation for being such cold, dismal lovers; such backward, stunted passionates?

"The English are so cold? Isn't that very old hat? I really don't know how you judge one person against another; or one race against another. Some are more different than others, that is all. I will not generalize. But how can the British be called

66

cold when they have produced some of the greatest lyric poets in the world? True, one cannot measure ordinary behaviour from poetry.

"If I *have* to generalize—and I hate it—I would say that Englishmen have bland faces. Underneath, they are absolutely seething. At the highest level, they are artists; at the middle level they are enigmas; at the lowest, they throw up the most intricate sexual villains and murderers in the world. And I'm not, of course, speaking of class.

"Chiefly, the most important characteristic is their refusal to get flustered. So how do you *know* what goes on underneath? I remember one evening, I was standing on Charing Cross underground station. A drunk on the platform opposite was having a ball. Everyone standing anywhere near him simply pretended he wasn't there at all.

"But all the people on *my* platform—where they were safe from contact with him—doubled up laughing at his antics.

"On the whole, I think the American is more of a kind of 'doer' when it comes to courting a girl. He'll take you out and show you things—endlessly. Spend a lot of money on you. They're pretty generous.

"The Englishman is much more likely to take you round the corner to a little bistro, more or less as an afterthought. I'm a non-planner myself, so that's the way I like it.

"I like their deviousness, and their dryness and their off-beatness. They get maudlin when they're drunk, though, and I don't like that much.

"You see, I can't really say much about the English because they're too idiosyncratic.

"Morally? Well, most people have their own traffic-light system, don't they?"

Which is all that Miss Suzman would say on the subject.

Miss H......'s thin, white hand was a mass of tiny blue veins just under the skin. She tapped the paper on her desk, between the annual hockey medallion and the globe presented by her last sixth form before she had come to the school as headmistress. "You *did* write it, didn't you, Candida?" she said. "I know I probably can't prove it; but I *would* like to know. Won't you tell me, please?"

The girl standing opposite, on the other side of the cluttered, red leather-topped desk, was almost boyishly thin. Her dark hair was cropped to a simple helmet, yet its starkness did nothing to diminish the attraction and power of a pair of heavily fringed dark eyes larger than is normally proportionate in a small face. All else in Candida R......'s outward appearance fell away by comparison. She was *all* eyes. Now, they were very wide and very innocent.

"Well, Miss H......, I did *write* it, yes," she said in a husky voice. "But I'd no idea they were going to put it in the magazine. Not like that, anyway. I just sent them what I'd written and expected them to use some part of it."

"Under your own name?"

"No. I specifically asked the editors not to mention me or the school. They promised they wouldn't."

"Well, they have kept their word, it seems, and thank Heavens for that. But, Candida my dear, how *could* you? I haven't read it all, but *really* . . ."

The girl became tauter under the rebuke. Her eyes had relaxed slightly, and the lustrous upper lids were halfway closed in a faint hint of scorn.

"It is all perfectly true, Miss H....... I believe every word of it."

"Well." Miss H......'s normally marble-still hand was tugging nervously at a corner of the paper. "You can't mean it!" She said it in a low voice. Her eyes were on the magazine. She raised this, and read from an open page.

" 'On the average, most of my friends have lost their virginity by the age of sixteen . . .' "

Candida interrupted: "That's not at school only. At home, too. It's true."

Miss H...... sighed. "And this? 'It is not unknown for girls to lose it at the age of twelve. But they are mainly precocious and have lost it through going out with boys considerably older than themselves—say nineteen to twenty-five. Boys whom I am in contact with tend to be non-virgins at the age of seventeen, and only the exceptions are before that age.' Is that also true?"

"Yes. I *did* know two girls in my form, when I was in IV B, who had been intimate with boys that much older. They were both twelve or thirteen. The girls, I mean."

"And how do you profess to know about the boys?"

For a second the eyes danced dangerously. "Oh, they tell me," she said. "Where I live, we're all pretty, well, matey. We talk about these things. And I've got two older brothers, you know."

Miss H...... drew in breath and continued reading: " 'I think that by the time a girl is seventeen and is still a virgin she begins to feel sexually incapable and says to herself, "Christ, is there something wrong with me? I must be frigid or something." About ten or fifteen years ago, non-virgins were looked down upon, but now non-virginity seems to be something of a status symbol. A boy who has never had intercourse by eighteen begins to be talked about, and is often said to be impotent or scared. The losing of his virginity is a great event in his life, because he thinks that he has now made the grade.' Is that also reported fact, Candida?"

"Well, it could have been better put, I suppose. But, yes, it's basically true."

"You're seventeen yourself, aren't you, my dear?"

The eyes were at their widest. "Yes, Miss H......."

There was a silence in which the soft ticking of Miss H......'s clock and the faraway sound of a teacher's voice raised in vigorous education could be clearly heard.

"I see," said the headmistress dryly.

... the experienced teenagers were asked: "Have you any idea why it happened?" ... Their replies reveal the big difference between the two sexes. The boys were most likely to reply that they were impelled by sexual desire (46 per cent) whereas the girls were more likely to say they were in love (42 per cent). This would confirm the suspicions of those who see the male as essentially a predatory animal whereas the female is amative and romantic. However, despite the difference in the two outlooks, both are intrinsically based on the sexual appetite, and indeed 16 per cent of the girls gave this as the reason. A large number of the boys (25 per cent) and quite a few girls (13 per cent) were driven towards their first experience for reasons that can best be summed up by the word *curiosity* ... Less than half the boys (48 per cent) and less than a third of the girls (30 per cent) said they liked it ... On the other hand 7 per cent of the boys and 7 per cent of the girls said they actively disliked it ... The boys were more likely to express their feelings in terms of pleasure and enjoyment, or the lack of it. The girls were more inclined to describe their later reactions after the sexual excitement was over. It is interesting to see that among the girls more were ashamed (25 per cent) than afraid (15 per cent) and even among the boys 10 per cent felt ashamed.

"The Sexual Behaviour of Young People",
Michael Schofield

The door slammed and Mrs Bonny R...... switched off the vacuum cleaner with her foot. Her head cocked on one side, she listened for the heavy crunch of her husband's regulation British Army boots on her tiled kitchen floor. "Is that you, Bill?" she called out. There was no reply. She went uneasily to the door of the lounge, leading to the passage. For about two seconds she stood, undecided, then a sound reassured her and she walked back, down the passage, towards the small kitchen in the rear. A man's shoulder, wearing battle dress was towards her, seated on the kitchen chair and taking his boots off. "Couldn't you answer me?" she said.

Her husband's head snapped up and he looked at her over his shoulder. Both eyes were red rimmed and his gaze was haggard. "Are you still here?" he asked in a thick "Scouse" accent. "I thought to find you packed off to your ma."

She sniffed and walked past him, none too daintily.

"You'll be wanting your lunch, I suppose," she said, her Dublin brogue more than usually pronounced. "What you swallowed for breakfast wouldn't hardly keep a crow alive."

"Ay. Well, there are other things more important than food . . ."

"Oh, for God's sake, Bill," she implored, "you're not going to start that all over again, now, are you? Didn't we just have enough of it all with our corn flakes this morning? And last night, when you came in filthy drunk from that sergeants' mess of yours. Didn't we stay awake till all hours arguing and carrying on? And you banging away all over the house! How Bridie slept through it, I'll never know. Do you want three sausages or two?"

"Three. And don't think you've heard the last of what we were talking about, my girl. I'm not finished by a long chalk, I can tell you that."

She was at the stove, her swelling, pregnant belly pressing against the metal front of it, a lighted match in her hand and the frying pan, with the pricked sausages neatly laid inside with a knob of lard, on the still unlit burner. Before she turned the tap she looked back at her husband where he sat in his stockinged feet, easing sweaty socks over his toes.

"And just what is that supposed to mean?" she asked. There was an ominous change in her voice, and the words came with rising intensity. "Am I supposed to understand that *you*, Mr Lord-bloody-God-Almighty, has something more to say on the subject of whether or not I'm to be made into some sort of animal, to satisfy *your* pleasure? Is that it, then?" Her tone changed, and she flicked out the match as it began to burn her fingers. "I'll have you know, my bhoyo, that no man on this God's earth is going to make *me* into a filthy beast fit only for the fields. And nobody, not your bloody Highness or anybody else, is going to make *me* renounce my God and his teachings

70

and use that filthy stuff to stop innocent babies coming into the world. I won't, do you hear. *I won't! I won't! I won't!*"

She was banging the stove with the cold pan, unconsciously. Her eyes filled with tears. She bowed her head and turned away from him, hiding her face. He sat glaring at the stockinged foot, unseeing it.

A long silence filled the small room. Then, with a weary gesture, she pulled herself upright, lit another match, ignited the gas with a loud *plop* and started to cook the sausages. He was behind her, on his unbooted feet, before she realized he was there.

"You'll do *what*?" he whispered in her ear. It was heavy with threat. "You'll just do bloody *what-did-you-say*?"

She swivelled as though stung by a poisonous insect. The hot pan was in her hand and her action in turning slopped some of the bubbling fat onto the stove. "Don't you touch me, you bloody great bully you!" She was screaming now, her eyes wide with rage and fear. "Get out of my way before I let you have this full in your ugly face." She brandished the hot pan.

"Just you try it," he said. "And I'll break every tiny, wee bone in your whole, stinking, useless body . . ."

Afterwards, she had no memory of having picked up the knife. She didn't see three-year-old Bridie in the door, holding her doll. She saw nothing but his face, his eyes closed to ugly, threatening slits. And the wave of blood-red horror she felt as he struck her full across the mouth with the back of his hand, cutting her lip with his gold eternity ring which she had given him on their second anniversary. The rest was silence and blind, unrecording hatred for the threat to more than her life, to the privacy of her love and obedience for God. She saw him wince sharply and watched her own fist plunge the blade straight into his chest, just above the pocket flap. There was no stain before he fell, and no sound except the choke in his suddenly arrested breathing. Then he was face down on her kitchen floor, the blood slowly streaming out from under him, the sausages burning and Bridie shrieking and running over to the body of her father. It was Bonny's twentieth birthday.

A young girl is listening to the juke-box at the American Soda Fountain in Whitewell Road, Belfast. She looks pensive as she eats a Hawaian Float. A boy walks over and asks her if something is wrong. "I've just been thinking," she says, "in eight years I'll be thirty—can you imagine anything so old?"

Report by Michael Braun, the OBSERVER

"You can't kid me the last generation were any more moral than we are. They hid it better. If you wheedle it out of people they were just as bad as we are only they grew out of it.

"Perhaps," he said, with the air of one hitting on the truth, "perhaps they grew too *tired* for it."

"Beatle" Paul McCartney—interviewed by Maureen Cleave,
EVENING STANDARD, *25 March 1966*

Chapter 9

12 noon

COME AND GET IT

"There's nothing *unreal* about having this attachment for your dog—being *in love with it*, if you like—Mrs T . . . . . . It *is* a little unusual. But you must not feel guilty about it. You don't feel that, do you?"

Dr de S . . . . . . was not having an easy morning. Even as he put the question, the climax of nearly half an hour's concentration on Mrs Noel T . . . . . .'s "problem", the telephone rang. He heard the bell sounding in the reception lobby and felt a rush of fury as he realized that Vivienne was not going to answer it. "Oh, do please excuse me," he mumbled, striding toward the door. He picked up the phone in the next room and managed a totally artificial relaxation of his voice as he spoke: "Hallo, Dr de S . . . . . .'s consulting rooms here."

"Is that you Julian?"

He recognized Ian's voice immediately. "Yes. Ian? Look, old man, I'm terribly tied up. It just happens there was nobody to answer the phone . . ."

"I won't keep you. Could you see somebody for me, fairly

soon? A young girl of twelve who's gone and got herself pregnant.
I think she may get into serious trouble . . ."

Dr de S . . . . . . kept control of his floating mind with an effort.
How could he possibly fit it all in? "Yes, yes of course," he said.
"Send her to me, Ian. Write her a little note, that's all, saying
she comes from you. I'll tell Vivienne to expect her. Which day
did you say?"

"If it's at all possible, I'd like you to see her *today*. I'm driving
up and could bring her along this evening. Any chance that
you're going to be free at about six-ish?"

"All right, Ian. I'll manage that somehow."

"Good man. Well, mustn't keep you now."

"No. See you later. Bye-bye."

Dr de S . . . . . . put down the phone and walked back towards
the woman he had left lying on the special couch on which
Vivienne slept. Without the bedding, its appearance had changed.
It was stronger and less cosy. Mrs T . . . . . . was sitting up, doing
something to her face with the aid of materials extracted from
a zebra-skin handbag and a small mirror.

"Oh Doctor," she drawled in the accent cultivated between
St George's Hospital rear entrance and the first hint of the slums
of the Brompton Road. "You are *such* a comfort to me."

Dr de S . . . . . . managed a pleased, infinitely professional smile.
"My dear Mrs T . . . . . .," he said silkily. "You must not concern
yourself with *me*. It is Science which can help you; and I am
happy to know that it is doing so. We owe it all to the great
Sigmund, you know."

"Oh, I *do* know. He was so *marvellous*. I can't understand
why people will still criticize him and his wonderful work. Well,
they'll discover one day what it all means," she ended vaguely.

"Indeed." Dr de S . . . . . . extended his arm and helped Mrs
T . . . . . . to her feet. She was no more than five foot two. His
bald head loomed over her like a rogue balloon. "Now, if you
will prepare yourself for another session next week at the same
time, I feel sure we will be able to analyse the reason for Brutus's
sudden hostility towards you. There *must* be a reason. Somewhere deep down."

She allowed him to help her into £5,500 worth of sable coat.
"I *know*. Isn't it most extraordinary? But I'm *sure* you'll discover
what is at the root of his behaviour. Dear Dr de S . . . . . ." She
held out her hand. "Next week, then?"

He saw her out himself, then poured a drink from a small,
white medicine-cupboard in the reception lobby.

74

What is woman, except in the power of him she loves? What are all the games and festivals where love is lacking? What is virtue with no peace of heart? Severed from caresses, how can there be joy?

The fruit of childhood is in liberty, the fruit of youth is in magnificent lusts, the fruit of age is in peace of soul; the fruit of life is to have laboured . . .

If but the union of hearts may be consummated in love games, let the world wag. For love is master, but his mastery lies in passion.

Translated from the "Kuttanimatum"

Sam S . . . . . . told himself for the umpteenth time that he would have to do something about it. For the umpteenth time plus one, he got no further with this thought. His wife, Edith, was a bitch; there was no doubt about that. She loathed him, what was more. And for the past three years, since he had accused her of entertaining the milkman in her kitchen (of which he had far more evidence than he had ever disclosed to her) she had made his life into an incessant torment.

Last night it had been itching powder in his bed. When he had finally succumbed to the unbearable irritation, and got up to take a bath—which only made it worse—she had, while pretending to be asleep, loosened the stopper in his hot-water bottle so that the bed was soaked when he came to get back into it. This morning as he was washing out some of his underwear, a necessity of his daily life since she had flatly refused to have anything to do with his laundry, she had screamed at him, gone practically berserk, and finally ripped out a sash cord from the kitchen window and tried to tie his arms with it. Failing to do this adequately, she had rampaged through the house ripping long strips of wallpaper off with her finger-nails whenever she found a loose edge or corner. Screaming all the while about his keeping her in penury, in this broken-down house, among these mangy bits of furniture; refusing ever to take her away, out of this squalor, or to do anything about improving his position; or showing the least little speck of a sign of love for her; all so loud and strident in tone that the neighbours on both sides could hear almost every word.

Now, as the bus took him along the crowded High Street, he saw from the clock in the Post Office window that he was going to be five minutes late, at least; his inside trembled. *"God, don't let her put my dinner out on the front lawn again, like last time,"* he prayed. Only a week ago she had dumped it under the bird bath and told him if he couldn't keep decent times like everyone else, when a woman had been slaving at a hot stove all morning,

75

then he could just damned well eat it outside with the other worms and animals. Then, after she'd gone back indoors with a slam of the front door that nearly took it clean off its hinges, she had returned a few minutes later with armfuls of his clothes —shirts, ties, shoes and his best suit—and dumped those down beside him, shrieking at him to "get out of my house and go and live with your sister or anyone else who'll have you!" He had been over half an hour late back to his desk in the Pensions (Supplementary) office at the Council Hall by the time he had managed to restore everything to some sort of order. And after she had calmed down a bit.

What *was* he going to do? She didn't really hate him, he felt sure of that. And he *couldn't*, not wouldn't, just walk out on her. The house, for a start, was his. He'd been paying the mortgage every month for the past twenty-three years, ever since their marriage, and in two years' time now he would have paid off the last of it: £1,600 then, and now worth double. But how could he go on?

She had taken all the furniture out of the spare room again last week and put it in at Eaveden's for the coming auction. He had had to make up a story about his mother coming to stay with them unexpectedly to get it back. Worse than that she was becoming daily more violent, less controllable in her fits of rage. He remembered the day she had gone for him with a poker (would he ever forget it?—it had been his birthday). But last week it had been a broken milk bottle, and he had grazed his hand, drawing blood, taking it off her.

It was his stop, the corner of Farley Road. He nodded to the conductress and got off, walking quickly up towards the furthermost of the identical, sooty, pebble-dashed "semis" in his row. Almost identical smoke curled dirtily out of all of them, but his. She would have none of the business of making a decent fire. He had to supply her with a succession of electrics, which she broke time and again by lighting her cigarettes directly from the elements.

At the gate, he was so nervous that he found the simple task of unlatching it awkward, and before he managed to reach the front door he was flustered. He was going round to the side so as not to disturb her when she flung it open in his face. She was a short, dark woman with untidy, nervy hair and eyes round as pebbles. Her mouth was thin and drawn and her face a mass of greasy lines. It was her clothing, though, which first came to notice. She wore a pair of men's trousers, held up by an old

76

child's skipping rope, and with the buttons of the fly plainly visible. They were stained and dirty and turned up at her ankles. She looked, in them, as though she had just been caught in the act of doing some perfectly filthy job for which she had borrowed a pair of old slacks from the man of the house. In fact, these were her everyday wear.

"A nice time," she barked at him. "Six minutes late again! What's it to be? No dinner, or that precious job of yours which earns us such a fortune, I don't think?"

He faced her with his hands drawn tightly down the sides of his legs, like an errant schoolboy, or a disciplined soldier. "Sorry, Edie," he said humbly. "We are very busy just now."

"Busy," she made the word abusive. "Any excuse to put *me* out. *I* don't matter, do I? Well, come in then and don't bother to wipe your feet."

There was something mysterious about the way she said this. His heart sank even further into his boots. *What had she done this time?* As he crossed the threshold and put his foot down in the hall he knew, with a start of real pain.

The hall carpet—a length of patterned Axminster he had saved more than eighteen months for—had gone. In its place were sheets of newspaper.

Our society is a society controlled by males—a patriarchy—in other words men enjoy the greatest privileges and decide more things . . . .
"An ABC of Love", Inge & Sten Hegeler (Spearman)

It is bad manners for a husband to kiss his wife unless he has shaved . . ·
A man who makes love and then turns over and goes to sleep without telling his wife how much he enjoyed himself is both a fool and a brute.
Barbara Cartland, as reported by the late Nancy Spain

They looked as though they had walked a long way as they came into the station from the goods ramp running beside Number One platform. Paddington was its usual self, a faded monument to past glories and a sweet smell of trains' lavatories. Arthur C. . . . . . was wearing a dirty fawn mack and his wife, Gladys, was in a shapeless brown overcoat with a piece of fur at the neck.

The children were pale and both boys had livid spots on their chins. Cilla, the elder girl, was pretty in a wild, ungroomed way, until she opened her mouth when she showed stained and broken front teeth. The other girl, who was actually slightly younger than the younger boy, Tom, but who looked older in her wobbling high heels and torn stockings, carried a small black-faced doll and a cheap handbag.

Mrs C...... carried the baby, which had a dummy in its mouth from which a piece of brown string hung across its shawl. It lay perfectly silently in her arms, its over-blue eyes wide open. It was another girl, eight months old and spastic.

They moved across the main hall of the station without curiosity. Nobody spoke. Arthur led the way, then the walking children and his wife at the rear. When they came to the open doors of the main buffet, he turned and looked at them without emotion. "Do what mother says," he told the girl, Cilla. She looked up at him, her mouth slightly open.

"When do we get collected?" she asked.

"It won't be long. Just wait there," he told her.

Gladys had come up and joined them. She opened her handbag and took out two half-crowns which she gave to the elder girl.

"'ere," she said, "Go'n buy them some chips and a cup of tea. Go on. Go in and sit at one of them tables and have what you fancy. Your dad and me'll be gone in a minute. You'll be all right, love, like we said. They'll collect you."

The girl's glance did not alter but in the back of her nut-brown eyes was an unspeakable agony.

"Won't we see you no more then?" she asked, "Mum?"

"Go on. You do what I say," said her mother, pulling at the baby's shawl nervously. "They'll collect you."

"Ta-ta, then."

They watched the children saunter into the busy tea and sandwich buffet without expression. The mother's haggard face turned to her husband.

"What do we do now?" she asked.

"Find somewhere to dump 'er." He pointed to the baby in its mother's arms. "Come on, you know." He started across the open space leading to the platforms. She hesitated for a few seconds. Then she followed him without looking back at her other children.

For about five minutes they prowled the large station like a pair of homeless vagrants seeking shelter. At a row of wooden seats somewhat hidden from the main thoroughfare he signalled to her with a quick, furtive gesture and she put the baby down in the corner. But as she was fussing over its shawl a man and a woman came up and sat down. After a short moment, she picked up the baby again and they walked away.

"Arthur," she said. "Do you think they'll be all right? *Reelly?*"

"They'll have to look after 'em, won't they?" he said. His voice was bitter as a desert. "Better'n we could, mother."

"I hope they'll be all right." she said plaintively.

They walked on, in silence.

At a row of empty telephone booths, they tried again. They managed this time to prop the baby in the corner on the small shelf holding the directories. But as she turned away, it began to cry and wave its tiny hands. A passing porter heard and looked over. They quickly picked up the baby and moved to the far platform.

For a while they sat on an idle luggage truck. The station was only fairly busy, but a big train was preparing to leave for Cardiff and another had just come in. People with highly polished shoes and brief-cases and fur coats and well-dressed children were coming through the barrier in a steady stream. Arthur C...... watched them all without expression. It was impossible to read his thoughts.

Perhaps it was the easy manner some of the passengers used towards the porters which gave him the final idea. *"Porter, do take this . . ." "Oh, and could you be very careful with . . ."* He nudged Gladys.

"Mother. Just walk over to that porter-feller—there, the young one wi' his back to us—and ask him to hold the nipper for a moment."

She got up, looking bewildered. "Which one? Ow, I see 'im." She walked over and he watched as she approached the man and spoke to him. He had his hands in his pockets and was arguing with her. Then he took out his hands and with obvious reluctance accepted the bundle. She walked back to her husband, the porter's eyes following her.

"What do we do now?" she whispered as she came up to Arthur. "We can't just walk away."

"Come on," he said gruffly. He took her elbow and piloted her in the direction of the exit to the underground. The porter was watching them, a worried look on his fair, young face, until they disappeared.

It was his promptness which spoilt Arthur's plan. Not two minutes after the couple had gone he made up his mind that they were not coming back. He thrust the baby into a mate's arms and ran for the tube subway. They were halfway down the escalator when he caught up with them.

"Heh! What you on about?" he asked indignantly. "You got your baby up there! You leavin' it, or something?"

Gladys burst into tears.

Chapter 10

1 p.m.

KINKY TIME

Hickory, dickory, dock, the mouse ran up the clock, the clock struck one: lunchtime. Who knows what else occurs as the single chime ruptures the virginity of afternoon? Each Sunday one sees steamed out of the week behind it by the "family" newspapers a putrefying succession of sordid doings, vicious events and follies (*de petitesse* as often as *de grandeur*), as surprising and shocking to see as the lice sent scuttling by hot pokers from the soldier's seams in trench warfare. Often, they show that Old Nick is no time watcher. His malpractices beat the clock of respectability hands and trousers down. A man goes to his woman as he goes to his victuals. His appetites are real, material things. They grow unless assuaged. They are not to be trifled with or put lightly aside. They can seldom be cheated.

So, at the first break in the working day, when offices and factories pour out staff like clouds of human dust, one can expect to see caprices which can roughly be grouped under the heading of love. For want of any other. If lust is more apparent, that too is love's servant; when not its master, or jester.

The crimes committed in love's name at this hour are many, and often delightful. The unexpected is always more enjoyable, once it has overcome scruple. There is a tang of adventure, a spice of the hunting season, about the one o'clock encounters.

Miranda was nearest the phone when it rang. She gave her client, a pink and rotund blonde, one strong push along her deltoid muscle and came out of the cubicle, wiping massaging oil off her hands on to a square of rough towelling. "I'll get it," she called in a shrill voice to the other girls. "All right, Mr Max, dear."

The phone in Reception was pink. "'ullo?" she said. "*Salon de santé* 'ere. 'oo's that?"

A man's voice, gruff and educated, yakked into her ear. "Yes, good. Now can you give me an appointment for this afternoon?"

"Ooooh. We're booked up, I think. 'oo's calling?"

"Er—W...... Mr W....... I live near-by and I want a massage, you know. Do you think you could possibly fit me in?"

"What was it you wanted, Mr W......?"

"Ah . . . Well. The works, what?"

"How do you mean, dear? I mean sir. Wasn't there nothing particular you wanted done, like?"

"I leave that to you, my dear. You're far more experienced at these things than I am. I expect you know what I want pretty well. If you've ever been in the Far East, eh? They know the form over there, don't you know."

"We only do body massage, Mr W...... And follow-ups from the clinic; you know, physio and all that lot. Is that what you wanted?"

"What I wanted, my dear, is a bit of the right sort of massage, which I'm told you can provide. I don't give a damn where it is, provided it is *the right sort*, do you follow me?"

"I'm afraid I don't. Shall I get the manager?"

"No. No. Listen, it's perfectly simple if you're experienced in these matters. I'm sure you're very good at it, by the sound of your voice. And I don't mind paying, y'know. I expect it to be expensive. If it's good, I don't mind, that is."

Miranda, perplexed and confused, was getting fed up. "If *what's* good?" she asked sharply.

"Well, I only expect a little excitement, you know. It's up to you how you work up to it."

"You dirty old bastard!" She slammed the pink phone down and stood looking at it, her irises ringed with a black circle of shocked fury. Mr Max L......'s voice sounded above the hum of the vibro machine in No. 3. "Who was it, dear?"

"Oh," she said. "Nobody. Only another of them nuts."

However little passion you may feel for a woman, provided your imagination has not run dry, if she be inept enough to say to you one evening, tenderly and bashfully: "All right; come tomorrow at noon. I shall be alone," you will be unable to sleep, and quite incapable of thought. After a morning of torment the hour strikes, and it is as if each stroke were reverberating through your diaphragm.

"Maxims of Love", Stendahl (*Merlin*)

The waiting had been terrible for Clive L...... after Yvette had rung to say she couldn't manage the evening rendezvous, but would be free at lunch-time. "Why don't you come 'ere, to my leetle flat?" she had asked him. He was overjoyed. They settled on 1.15, because she said she had some shopping to do.

He stood now, in the concierge's lodge, feeling both guilty and stupid with the bottle of champagne in the carrier bag at his side and the bunch of purest, deep-red roses. The concierge had not emerged, but his gross, squat wife made it adequately plain that respectable people in Paris did not like to be disturbed during the *midi*.

She had used the ancient telephone in her parlour and he could hear the conversation. A woman's voice on the other end was first querulous and then assertive. The wife of the concierge put down the receiver, pushed a strand of dingy hair out of her eyes and beckoned him in the direction of the lift.

"Quatrième étage," she said. *"Madame vous attend."*

Clive, by dint of much patient fumbling with the complicated, slow and awkward controls of the lift and its iron gates, found his way to the destination. She was waiting for him in a soft, filmy négligé. He could hardly believe his eyes. In the hallway of the apartment she took his overcoat and hat, accepted the flowers with a soft "mm!" of delighted surprise, agreed to put the champagne on ice, then led him deliciously into the room on the right.

Three men, sprawled in armchairs in front of a fire reading newspapers and smoking, looked up and rose to be introduced. "My brothers," she said. "Zey are all of zem, what you say, poleece detecteeves."

Clive shook hands in frigid silence. The men seemed to regard his advent as a boring interruption. Yvette was as alluring as ever—more so—but now suddenly unattainable. What was he to do? He looked hurriedly at his watch.

"Oh, my God!" he said abruptly, in accents of heavy over-acting. "I have forgotten a most important business appointment. Please do forgive me, all of you. I must dash. Some other time…"

And sweeping his overcoat and hat off the chair in the hall he made for the lift. At the third floor, he distinctly caught the sound of a champagne cork freed from the neck of its bottle, and mannish laughter in which a woman's peal of mirth—far more English than he would have imagined, coming from such a French little thing as Yvette—led the guffaw.

What is virtue? "I have but a very confused idea of what virtue really is," observes that amiably candid strumpet of the Regency, Harriette Wilson. "Now the English Protestant ladies' virtue is chastity. There are but two classes of women among them. She is a bad woman the moment she has committed fornication; be she generous, charitable, just, clever, domestic, affectionate … the Protestant world will have it that all are virtuous who are chaste, even when chastity is to their liking—the selfish, the hard-hearted, the cruel mother, the treacherous friend, the unfeeling mistress—all! all! are called virtuous who are supposed chaste."

> *"The Girl With the Swansdown Seat"*
> *Cyril Pearl (Fredk. Muller)*

Life had not been kind to Detective-Sergeant Hubert L......
His day off, it was supposed to be. A day he had mentally scheduled for lying in; late breakfasting; running down to the coast, and spending the rest of the daylight and many subsequent hours with a lady of his acquaintance who ran a small seafront club. Chemmy and blackjack were played there until the early hours.

As it was, Molly would be disgusted with him. He had only just got back to the Yard and was about to go home when the call came in from a bright, over-zealous young plainclothes constable he had put on to watching a renowned call-girl's place in the West End.

"She's in there, Sergeant, with her husband, or ponce, or whatever he is. And the customers seem to be arriving by appointment. I've found a place at the back, on some fire-escape stairs, where we can get a good view of the whole thing. You asked me to ring you, before making an arrest."

"That's right," he said, cursing inwardly. "I'll be right down. Meet me at the pub on the corner in fifteen minutes."

It was as young Detective-Constable R...... had said. The place on the staircase provided an excellent vantage point for viewing all that went on in the first-floor flat opposite. Through his binoculars, Detective-Sergeant L...... could see that she was a buxom redhead, probably in her late thirties. He watched with complete absorption while she entertained a man with a white bald patch shining like a full moon in the centre of his dark hair. They were hardly undressed before they were putting their clothes on again. And in the next room her "husband" was eating a plateful of fish and chips which he had unwrapped from a newspaper parcel. The bald-headed customer hurried out of the flat, leaving two fivers.

"She's overcharging," said L...... admonishingly. The young constable did not smile. "I've had a look at the way in," he said. "We can turn them over fairly easily while the next one's on the job, Sergeant."

"That's what we'll do, then," said L....... "But let's wait till he's in the gaff first, shall we?"

For about ten minutes the man and the girl were alone. She did her hair at a mirror. He went solemnly on munching his meal. The two detectives climbed higher, to where they could just hear what was being said.

"How did you do last week, when I was away?" the man asked. He had a faint tinge of Mediterranean shores in his voice.

"Here," she said, "I've written them all down. A hundred and five nicker all together. Bit quiet, really."

"Never mind," he said. "We've done over the grand since we started in this pad, only two months and a half ago. I'm not complaining, love."

"He'll be here in a mo'," she said. "Mr bleeding Kinky."

"Oh, him," said the man at the table. "Well, never mind, love. The kinky ones always pay better, you know. How many does he want?"

"It depends on me, not 'im," said the girl firmly. "I gives 'im what I feel like. If I'm feeling cheeky, like, all right and good luck to them. I'll let 'im 'ave three today, maybe, for two quid apiece."

The man said nothing. Detective-Sergeant L...... motioned to R...... and the two of them descended the iron stairs, lifting their shoes carefully to avoid scraping.

They moved back to their earlier vantage point and took up position. Now that Hubert L......'s eyes were accustomed to the pattern of light, there was no need for the glasses. He stuffed them in his overcoat pocket.

At 1.46 by his wrist-watch a man came into the flat and was received by the woman in the small passageway which served as a hall between the bedroom and the sitting room where the woman's ponce had finished off his plate of food and was lighting a cigarette. The man who had come to the flat was short and dapper. He was middle-aged, neatly and expensively dressed. He carried a black leather dispatch case which, to the detectives' eyes, looked as though it had emanated from some Government department. It was voluminous and he had no sooner been shown into the bedroom and taken off his hat and coat than he opened it on the bed. The girl was beside him. She accepted some articles which he took out of the case and moved over to the dressing table. She took off her dress. Underneath, she was wearing white panties and bra. She had a good figure, Detective-Sergeant L...... noted.

The man was also undressing. He folded his trousers tidily and placed them on a low chair. His jacket was suspended over the chair's back. He unbuttoned his shirt down the front precisely, then took that off. In his underwear he looked even smaller.

Now, he unrolled a dark bundle which he had taken from the case. It became a short black dress such as maidservants and waitresses wear. He put it on, then added white starched apron, lacy black stockings and high-heeled shoes.

The woman had also dressed in the garments given her. Her costume was that of a rather grand English lady at the turn of the century in the White Raj of India. The dress could more justifiably have been called a gown. It draped itself almost to the floor and was of some satiny material with beads and tassels. Finally, she donned long, white gloves.

He was on his hands and knees in the middle of the room, moving his head up and down like a supplicating dog. The woman walked over to the bed and picked up a short whip. On the stairway, Detective-Sergeant L...... nudged his assistant and they moved stealthily, but fast, to ground level. From there it took only a few seconds to reach the front entrance to the flats. They went in and made for the second floor at the double.

Hubert L...... had played rugby for Blackheath until his accident. Hooker. He put a well-muscled shoulder to the door and it sprang open. They were in the small passageway with a naked light bulb blazing from a cord in its centre.

For a second or two they paused to get their bearings. Music was coming from the room on the right. Then from the left-hand room they heard an educated man's voice scream. "Yes, madam, I've been wickedly naughty. Punish me! Punish me!"

"You take that, R......," said L....... He wrenched open the right-hand door and disappeared inside. Detective-Constable Wilfred R......, just 22, was never going to forget the scene which greeted his eyes as he went into the room on the left.

The man in the black stockings and maidservant "drag" was full length on the fitted carpet. The woman was standing over him, the whip raised in her hand.

She had pulled up the man's skirt and exposed his bare buttocks. There were already two livid, red weals across them. While she beat him with all her force, the man on the ground was kissing, or licking, her shoes.

If Auberon Waugh is to be believed, this is also the hour when fair-minded young office girls must pay for their luncheons. In his novel *Who Are the Violets Now?* (Chapman & Hall, 1965) there is a particularly crude reminder of this. Ferdie, a junior advertising executive, has taken Nina, a co-worker, to lunch. He watches her afterwards, suspiciously. In Mr Waugh's words:

Had she forgotten who had paid for the lunch?

'Where shall we go?' he said.

Nina looked up, met his eyes and smiled. She was not one to shirk her obligations, although the spaghetti and ice-cream rather lay heavy on her stomach.

'We could go in the Ladies.'

'Are you mad? What on earth would people say if they saw me coming out of there? That's the trouble with this office, there's nowhere to go when you want some fun.'

'We could use Mr Isinglass's room. He won't be back 'til after three. There's a carpet.'

'And get me the sack? Thank you very much.'

In the end, they decided on the Gentlemen's lavatory. Ferdie locked the door and whispered:

'It's too cramped to do anything in here.'

'Not at all,' said Nina, adjusting herself and resourcefully climbing on the pedestal.

Once again, youth showed the way.

At least, according to Mr Waugh, it did so.

Chapter 11

2 p.m.

NUTS AND WINE

We are at the nuts and wine stage; the post-prandial beginnings of afternoon, man's most lethargic ebb. The business of loving is not interrupted—it never is—but the spirits tend to be less resilient. There is an amatory torpor in the atmosphere under the low-scudding clouds of an English sky. At this time of year, two hours separate us from darkness and the soft awakenings of passions. Now, we must peer into strange places to find love's face.

It is in a Black Maria, leaving Clerkenwell Magistrates Court, where a little runt of a man is going the way of his tribe: those who live on the immoral earnings of women. Ernie D...... is only different from his kind in one way: he loves the woman he sold to other men. Sitting here in the locked van beside the other convicts, ugly men, smelling of fear and degradation, he nurses the hurt which is his separation from Mary. She is his wife.

When he sees her again, in fifteen months' time if he behaves himself, she will have had the baby. Or not. That depends on her now.

They had agreed to go through with it when she first found she was pregnant. There was no doubt about it being his. She had not been working, due to her illness, for six weeks beforehand. And she wanted the baby dreadfully, she said.

He had had to put her back on the game when the betting shop folded; and *she* hadn't complained. Who'd complain? *A hundred nicker a week!* That's what she'd been making for the past six weeks. If she hadn't made such a song and dance about it the neighbours wouldn't have got onto them. He wouldn't be here now.

The van gave a slight shudder as the driver pressed the starter. The motor fired; they were away. Ernie sat in the corner made by the rear door and the outer side of the van. He could hear traffic passing. His mind drifted back to the day—last Sunday—when she'd gone too far.

He was outside in the car, as usual, having run the sucker up to their house. "Avalon" stood by itself in a small row of similar detached dwellings. It was unpretentious and the garden was run down and seedy; but the road was not without a certain social standing. A doctor had his nameplate on the gatepost of No. 3, on the far side.

She wasn't long with this one. He still had time to hear the rest of Saturday's racing results on the car radio before going off for the next on his list. They got the addresses after they telephoned, and he always picked them up in person. It was his idea, that. "It would look funny, wouldn't it, if all those blokes kept coming up in different motorcars? They'd know we were in *some* sort of business."

He had told her that before they'd started. She'd sniffed. "Yeah, monkey business. Ought to mind their own bleeding business, that lot," she'd said.

It was the one trouble with Mary. A lovely girl; and as good as gold. But something in her nature, maybe the Irish blood she got from her mother, made her *hate* nosey-parkers.

She had come walking down the unswept drive towards him, smiling, as the last customer made his way along the road on foot. It wasn't part of Ernie's plan to drive them away again. Provided they paid up and behaved like gentlemen, nobody was going to make any trouble for them. But they needn't expect molly-coddling.

"Hallo, ducks," he said. "Just wait while I hear whether Heather Snap made it in the 3 o'clock. I still fancy that nag."

She leaned silently on the car door, drawing on her cigarette.

After a few moments, he switched off the radio and turned to her. "Give us a ciggy, love," he said. She handed him a packet from the pocket of her jersey suit. It was lemon-coloured with white cuffs and collar and a black tie-string at the neck. "When's the next?" she asked.

"He can wait a minute or two," Ernie told her dispassionately. "Don't worry, he will." He grinned at her, meaning it as a compliment. It was his way to flatter women.

"I feel so tired," she said. "I'd like a nice, long sleep. Or a holiday, even. Wouldn't that be nice, though, Ernie? Why don't we go away from this dump, somewhere where it's warm?" She shivered.

"The money's good here," he remonstrated. "Besides, we've got the rent to pay, whether we use it or not. That toffee-nosed agent wouldn't let us take it on less than a quarter's rent down and the rest in advance.

There was the noise of a gate being slammed with unusual ferocity. The woman who lived on the right of "Avalon", in "Sunnymeade", came towards them with a grim set to her plain face. She was wearing dark clothes and was probably, Ernie thought, watching her in the driving-mirror, on her way to visit somebody's grave. What was her name? Ah, yes: Mrs C. . . . . . .

She stopped beside them. It was as though she felt unable to avoid contact. Her back was rigid, her eyes, small and angry. And her voice, when she spoke, had an underlying quiver of hostility. "I see you keep *plenty* of male company, even on a *Sunday*," she said icily. "You must have *ever so many* friends, Mrs D. . . . . . . They all look *different* to me!"

The affront was more in the veiled accusation behind her words than in their meaning. Mary stiffened. She took the time, while taking a deep drag on her cigarette, leaving a vivid ring of scarlet lipstick on the butt, to look Mrs C. . . . . . up and down with the insolence and suppressed violence of a rutting cat.

"And *what*," she began slowly, "in hell's bloody name has it got to do with you, Mrs . . . . . . ?"

The other woman only glowered, holding her ground. The two were like game-birds feeling for an opening. Between them, the air lay heavy with tension.

"Do you think I'm a *tart* or something, is that it?" Mary asked shrilly. "Because, if you do, you're bloody well right, darling. I am! I bloody well am! And what are you going to do about it? Eh? What are you going to do about it, you poor miserable old thing? Do you want to know what I earn, do you? Tell her Ernie.'

Ernie stayed silent. He had one hand on the door handle ready to pounce if Mary started throwing her weight. He'd seen her in a fight with another girl who'd tried to pinch her beat in Lyle Street, when he'd first met up with her, before the new Act drove all the girls off the streets. It wasn't a pretty sight, and he'd never forget the tufts of skin and blood and hair she had taken out of her finger nails afterwards.

"All right then," she said. "*I'll* tell you. A hundred quid a week! *Darling!* Do you think *you*, or any of your kind, could earn that sort of money?" She snorted in the other woman's face. "*You*," she said, "would be lucky if a man would pay sixpence to kiss your arse."

Mrs . . . . . .'s face had drained of blood. She turned on her heel as if a large, invisible hand had seized her shoulders and pivoted her. Head high, she marched off. Only when she was at the corner did she look back. "You'll hear about this," she shouted. Her voice sounded strangled.

Mary laughed. "Silly old cow!" she said. But Ernie knew then that the game was up.

I'd been working in that factory five years before I realised I was sitting on a fortune all the time.

Prostitution, like everything else in England, is shot through with class values . . .

One way on to the game is even before they come to London. A girl who has been easy at school—not generally because she likes sex but because she wants to find out if it isn't possible to like it more—takes work as a waitress or chambermaid at a provincial hotel. She sleeps with the odd commercial traveller, and then one day one of them gives her a pair of nylons. The next one gives her a pound to buy her own, and the penny drops. She's been paid for it. Next stop London, and the big money.

Three quotes from Wayland Young's
article in ENCOUNTER, *May 1959*
"The Prostitute in London"

These "ladies of easy virtue" as they are also called, are thus not particularly happy or easy-going people. Nor are they particularly passionate girls combining the useful and profitable with the pleasurable—on the contrary, their share of erotic pleasure is particularly small and a number of them are moreover homosexual.

Nobody knows why some become prostitutes and others not. All we can observe is that some take the moral laws of society more lightly than others. Various theories have been put forth. One of them is to the effect that prostituted women are supposed to have felt themselves unwanted as children, and in their unhappy, distrustful and continuously disappointed yearning for warmth and love have slipped into letting money be a substitute.

At any rate it is quite definite that masses of girls, before, now and in the future, solely on account of their external attractions, will earn money, acquire influence and get married. They will get given big parts for going to bed with the director or just because we like watching them undress in a rather piquant way in front of everybody. No education or other qualifications are necessary. It is so easy to moralize. Let us leave it to those whose past entitles them to do so. Let us make do with admitting that if we men were able to get ourselves jobs as directors, professorships—or wherever our ambitions may lie— by being obliging to influential ladies (who have no need to be repulsive on that account) many a business concern and faculty would have a different leadership today.

Or perhaps a more extensive leadership.

"An ABC of Love", Inge & Sten Hegeler

The saloon of the Dog and Duck was in full session; talk going well, atmosphere nicely clogged with pipe and cigarette tobacco smoke, pints being reduced at a comfortable speed. And Bill A......, the young representative of Fysher and Steed, was standing quietly by the covered dart-board talking to his friend Ted T.......

"I work hard, I don't mind admitting, Ted. But my wife works *much* harder than I do. I've realized it these last two days, while I've been at home looking after my older one, with my wife in hospital. You never stop, for a minute, from first thing in the morning to last thing at night. If the baby picks up a knife in the garden, you're frightened all the time she'll fall on it, or something. When you put her to bed at night, as I have been doing, and put her down, you know, you have to go up again every few minutes to see if her legs are sticking out of the cot. Or maybe she'll have her pillow down at the bottom of the cot. I tell you, it makes me livid. I get really mad sometimes. I want to give her a right healthy smack. Then she lies on her little back and says "Hi-ya, dad," and you can't do a blessed thing.

"Marriage, Ted, is very good in those ways. You can't beat it, quite honestly. But my advice to a fellow like you—or for that matter to any single man—is to leave it as long as possible.

"Why? Because you've no idea what you're going into, old man. I didn't know. Not the faintest.

"I tell you, I've got a friend with an M.G., a bachelor, he's got mistresses in Cornwall, South Wales, London, everywhere . . . Each weekend, he's only got to pick up the phone and he's away. Now that chap is as well-off as I am; better. But, honestly speaking, you can't say he has my worries, can you?

"No, you can't beat marriage, Ted, when you're ready for it. I mean, you don't have to go out every night like you used to. You can sit at home and watch television. That's what I like to do. But you want to leave it as long as you can.

"I'll never forget when this insurance agent calls, just before Betty went into hospital. I went to the door feeling pretty big, I can tell you. My own house, wife in the kitchen, baby on the way, everything paid for. And this man just said: "Hallo sonny, is your mother at home?" I damned nearly hit him."

Chapter 12

3 p.m.

TIME, GENTS

It was not a particularly savoury pub. He had only meant to drop in for a quick gill of scotch and a look at the paper before going on into Glasgow. This was an unfamiliar district to him and he always felt slightly apprehensive when out of his local environment. But there was also the slight tug of excitement at not being known or recognized as a minister of the church. He had to admit that.

Without his clerical collar, he might be just anybody else. The knowledge gave him an illicit joy quite out of keeping with its potential. He had deliberately worn mufti all the time he had been staying with his wife's sister in White Craigs. Nobody had commented on the fact, but he knew they believed he did so out of tact for them; to avoid questions in front of the children; to make them all feel easier, as if he was just like one of them.

He had to admit, in his innermost heart, that the reason was nothing of the sort.

As soon as he had gone into the pub, something of its garish warmth and noisy, welcoming hum of conversation and laughter caught him to it. He drank the first glass of whisky alone and unnoticed. But by the second the young man in tweed trilby and heavy, mournful spectacles was exchanging the time of day with him. As usual, his accent gave him away.

"You from 'merica, then?" the man asked.

"Canada," he said.

"Aha. My a'ntie's boy ..." he launched into an anecdote about a young engineer from Motherwell who had made good in Ontario; it was a story James A . . . . . . had heard a dozen times since the start of his holiday, and he could almost guarantee the admiring climax of the Scottish native attraction for fresher and more lustrous fields: "Aye, oh aye. There's money to be made o'er there, right enough."

"Will you no' ha'e another?" the man asked.

A . . . . . .'s demurrance was superficial. He respected the rules well enough not to refuse too strongly. The amber liquid added its own touch of warmth to the occasion as he swirled it gently in the stemmed glass.

Two drinks later, he knew that he was in the company of Angus F . . . . . ., a lathe setter and capstan operator from Greenock who was on short time due to the "tairrible hard times" in the ship-building industry. His companion was in his early thirties, a widower like himself, and unattractive. His eyes were close-set and small, lending his whole face a suspicious and grudging air. In the way he had learned of reading people's characters from their expression, the Reverend A . . . . . . recognized a weak bully who was at his most genial when the world was treating him harshly. A fair-weather friend.

Just before the landlord called "time", the questions took a more personal turn. "Wha' brings you down here, then?" A . . . . . . was asked. He explained that he had come looking for some old books he needed. The second-hand bookstalls in this district were famous in the the city.

Now they were both outside the pub, in the greenish mist of the Scottish afternoon which, at this time of year, almost merged into night. F . . . . . ., plainly, had nothing to do. The whisky was warming both men's bellies. A girl passed on stiletto heels. From his piggy little eyes, the man watched her go by without changing his expression noticeably. But he had somehow become wolfish. A growling sound came from the depths of his throat. "No' bad," he said. "I wouldna' mind someth'n' like that this after-noon."

James A . . . . . . lit a cigarette with insolent abandon. At home

95

he hardly ever smoked, certainly not on an open street corner like this. "Aye," he said shortly. "I wouldn't mind a piece of tail myself."

"Come along then, man. What are we waitin' for?"

Afterwards, try as he might, he could not recall the route they had taken at F......'s suggestion. The man had known "a place", as he put it. In their excited, bored and mutually desirous state, they had accepted the needs of the occasion without question. If A...... felt qualms about his temporarily neglected cloth, he kept them to himself. His feet were their own master.

Somewhere in an area of rough pavements and tall tenements the colour of dried blood they had turned into a narrow side-street.

The "place" was halfway down. They were in a dark, unlit cement hallway, climbing innumerable stairs, all smelling of food and dirt. At a plain door, on either the fourth or fifth floor, F...... knocked. There was a long pause before a woman's voice called the question: "Who's there?"

"Friends," said F...... thickly. The whisky and the walk in the cold air were having their effect. Both men swayed slightly as they adjusted to the small landing. A lock scraped and the door opened about four inches. A woman's face appeared at about the level of A......'s middle waistcoat button. A small girl. She asked: "Does m' ma know you, then?"

"Tell her it's Billy," said F...... shortly. The girl opened the door. "Come on in," she said. "She'll be ready in a minute."

They stood in the passageway, until the girl led them into a small, crowded room on the right. She was doing sums in a book at the table with the wireless, tuned to Luxemburg, playing dance tunes in her ear. A gas-fire burned and a tabby cat sprawled in front of it.

They sat down in easy chairs, feeling roguish and awkward. The girl was about eleven. She had a large mole on her left cheek and a hare-lip. Her hair was red, like a fresh carrot, but without brightness. Under the table, A...... could see her feet pushed into worn slippers.

"She won't be long," the girl assured them. "She's just set me this homework to do." And then, as if in apology for paying them such scant attention. "If I don't do them right, y'know, she gets awfu' cross."

Modern Britain is a heathen country with family life in decline and young people contemptuous of the Church ... The kind of teenagers

96

I see have a knowledge of the facts and mechanics of sex, but it is not set against any kind of ethical background at all . . . They just hang about street corners and parks—there is no other point or purpose to their lives. I do not know what the cure is.

Mrs J. V. Rennie, Woman Inspector,
Birmingham City Police

Women's reasons for getting married were no longer quite so strong. Nowadays a woman could support herself and avoid having children . . . she felt a certain sympathy for men. They weren't involved directly. They could only stand and watch the women disappearing unless they were very wise and very strong. Personally, she'd been brought up to think of marriage as something ideal and wonderful, she couldn't get used to the reality as she saw it. It was her own fault that she couldn't adapt but there were so few men worth adapting for . . .

Eleanor Bron (in an interview with Marshall Pugh),
DAILY MAIL

The time was 3.21 by the big clock over the jewellers. Liverpool was quiet. A tug hooted on the river and a typist with almost white-blonde hair, high up in the Liver Building, gave an indifferent wave of acknowledgement. In the street, by the small cinema, the man stood with something under his shortie mack. When she came out, tossing her dark head and half running, awkwardly because her heels were high and her coat was only round her shoulders, held in front by two fingers, he moved as quickly as a sparrow in the path of a car. She was only half-way across the cobbled street, glassy in the cold mist, when he was up with her. One of his hands caught her shoulder and swung her round. She gave a sharp cry like a bird. Then the thing under his mack was out and he had brought it to his middle with both hands so that it pointed directly at her left breast. There was a loud roar and then another. The girl crumpled, her body sagged and fell to the street as though strings holding her up had been suddenly cut. She fell on her face, but a corner of the loose coat folded back and showed the uniform she wore as an usherette underneath. He looked down at her for a moment in the awful stillness of her death, then threw down the shotgun and ran not knowing where.

"I could never do the things that Englishmen do," said Princess Ira von Furstenburg to Susan Barnes of the *Sunday Express*. "They're much more morally free . . . I could never cope with all those intrigues in life. It is nerve-wracking. It is morally wrong, in my opinion. They have very little restraint in England. Actually, they are immoral . . . I believe Englishmen are morally much freer than we are, but they are very cold . . ."

"Tell me," Princess Ira von Furstenburg asked Victor Sims of the *Sunday Mirror* two months later, "is it so that an Englishman does not mind that a girl has been loved before?" The Princess added, with conviction: "No—if an Englishman loves, he does not care what has gone before."

Immoral? Cold? Uncaring about "damaged goods"? Is that the English lover? The Princess may think so. She is entitled to her opinion, as we may judge her own capabilities from the two unsuccessful attempts she has so far made at marriage (neither with an Englishman). But what is the whole story? On the grubby face of it, England at three in the afternoon is not a chivalrous, rapturous or romantic spot. It is grey and grim and, despite the moistness of everything, dehydrated. It looks shrunken, like prison clothing; lifeless as twigs.

Is this only another of its disguises? An urban one at that? In the country there is no diminution of the rhythms and passions that keep life's tides flowing; yet nobody should be misled by the town either, it seems. Perhaps it does give an impression of stale crusts, but that is only its exterior. On the inside, life is still throbbing and pulsing away. Not always pleasantly for those concerned . . .

As the lift was empty when she got into it at the mezzanine floor, where her agent's office was, Sally took out a comb and a mirror and activated a few strands of her chestnut hair. She wasn't looking her best today. No wonder Mr J . . . . . . had been so abrupt with her. But, anyway, the part in the film at Shepperton wouldn't have suited her. She couldn't be a teenager *all* her life. All the same, she wished he hadn't made it quite so rudely obvious that she was past it.

As the doors closed, she straightened the top of a nylon stocking, then rubbed a tiny smear of lipstick off one extremely white front tooth with a finger. *Saucy!* she thought. And not even one of his artificial, horrible, stinking kisses when she came in, either. He'd better watch it, had Sam J . . . . . . He wasn't the only theatrical agent in London and she knew how to get in with one just as big if she chose.

She flexed her middle to adjust her suspender belt, then turned demure, baby-blue eyes towards the doors as the lift slowed and stopped at the third floor. She had pressed the button for the sixth, wanting to visit the Ladies. Somebody else must have halted it on the way up.

The doors hummed for a moment, then burst open strongly. A young man with a quiff of blonde hair and side whiskers, incongruous on a thinly-boned, pimply face, sauntered in. He put both feet apart and raised his hands to his hips under his jacket, displaying a purple waistcoat with worked silver buttons. The doors remained open. He studied them impatiently, then turned his head in her direction.

"Going up, I hope?"

"I pressed for the sixth."

"Well, let's hope . . . ah, there we are."

The doors swung to and with a lurch the lift started to ascend. She noticed that he was looking at her. She glanced across and was astonished at the heat of his glance. When she dropped her eyes, she knew that he was still glaring at her. The knowledge made her feel suddenly weak at the knees. The lift was slowly ascending, but there were still several seconds to elapse before it would reach her destination. She felt a clutch of fear.

He moved his feet slightly and was beside her, his arm stroking across her back. She felt terror and anger well up in a molten amalgam, only checked by an odd curiosity to see what he would do next. As the lift bumped to a stop, he drew his arm tight round her waist and pulled her to him. His kiss was as hot as his glance, and she squirmed under it. Then the doors were opening and he had let her go. Before she screamed.

The woman most ripe for seduction in your circle is the woman fifteen years older than you are—especially if she was thought a great beauty fifteen years ago.

Alan Brien, the SPECTATOR

Chapter 13

4 p.m.

BLUE FOR A BOY

I have seen a worldly New Yorker shocked by our afternoon pleasantries in Soho, London. He found it impossible to imagine men with the stomach for blue films and girlie shows at four o'clock in the afternoon. It was hard to convince him that there was custom all round the clock of a British day and night for such items. And custom brings out the pimps and spivs and ponces.

This one was no seedier, no shiftier, than his type. He could not have been more than twenty-three. He seemed immensely sure of himself, and perhaps experience had taught him that all men are drawn by the sirens' song. "Do you fancy a film showing a real gay time?" he asked from the pavement edge, without even bothering to lower his voice. "From Paris? All new. All blue. We'll be taking the curtain up in a few moments now. Only two quid?"

Along the street, men stood, with the curiously still shyness of their sex, inside a small, rickety bookshop. Under the lure of erotic stimulation in goodness knows how many dark corners of their lives, they pawed books on the racks and counters. Those braver than others paid banknotes for envelopes of photographs, many of them taken in the period between the wars. For women or men alone in alluring poses, ten shillings. With partners, one pound. And a special set of fantastically uncomfortable-looking orgies, including black men and white women and animals, a fiver.

This sort of putrid traffic has been going on for as long as life in human form. Nutcracker man, if he had implements at all, probably used one of them to scratch an erotic design on a tree. Great wits and aristocrats have had a passion for collecting erotica, and nobody other than the psychiatrists has ever been able to explain why. Or why the Chinese prefer their pornography drawn meticulously on silk, while the British seem quite happy with "dirty postcards".

When the good folk of Peterborough were celebrating Britain's victory over her enemies on V.E.-night, women sewed Union Jacks to the crutch of their bloomers, then lifted their skirts to dance "*Knees Up Mother Brown*" in the locked back-parlour of a pub. They knew what men want.

Doctors throughout Britain are alarmed at yet another startling increase in the number of babies born to unmarried mothers. I can reveal that a report, soon to be released, shows a record total of illegitimate births—exceeding even the "black years" of the war. The latest yearly figures will disclose that the total of more than 63,000 babies born out of wedlock overtakes for the first time the previous shameful record of 1945.

                         Peter Forbes, writing in THE PEOPLE, *January 1966*

The B.B.C. man was in great form. Interviewing scores of people, of all sorts and conditions, leaves few illusions. He had a shrewd grasp of what the English feel about loving, and lusting. He had seen into many private worlds. And he told me with great conviction that "I should think 90% of the married men in top society in London play around. We may not have a reputation for keeping mistresses, like the continentals, but I'm damn sure there are more kept here than anywhere else. It's not only the men who play around, it's their wives as well."

On the other hand, the B.B.C. man was slightly sickened by the sentimentality of British people he sometimes came across, as shown for the objects of their love and devotion. People who write poems to small dogs sent up in space craft . . . traffic wardens who write poems to small children they dote on . . . everyone

101

who writes poems to anything or anybody without excuse of deep passion.

"I think *class* matters tremendously in analysing our attitude to love-making," he said. He didn't say that sex was "too good for the masses", but his opinion reminded me of that old joke. "It doesn't matter," he said, "whether a chap is a Frenchman or an Englishman or an African, provided he has the same or roughly the same background, education and that sort of thing. If they have about the same intellectual standards, then there will be less difference between them than between British people of different classes."

Then he recalled for me the immortal moment when, in a Cairo officers' club bar during the war, a beautiful but somewhat disappointed Syrian Jewess bitterly defined her English friends' capabilities as lovers:

"The whole trouble wiz you is your silly balls," she said, in an atmosphere of stunned surprise. Having finished her drink, she turned with fiery, dismayed eyes to explain to an attentive group:

"If you were not always running after zem, kicking zem, biffing zem against zee wall, and throwing zem about zee field, you would not be so exhausted zat you *cannot* make love!"

Perhaps not for the first time, the Englishman's legendary love of sport had earned him a curious epitaph as a lover.

A look passed between Dr Julian de S...... and his wife. "I suppose you know who *she* is," Vivienne said darkly. "Your four-thirty appointment. Miss Doreen T........ You know what *she* did?"

Dr de S...... was writing at his desk. He did not like to be interrupted while compiling his notes, which he regarded as a most important part of his case-work. "Yes, dear," he said vaguely. "She murdered somebody, or something, wasn't that it?"

"She was acquitted."

"Ah, yes. Well, show her in, would you?"

Mrs de S...... went out and a tall, rounded woman with strikingly dark eyes came into the consulting room. She had a small, old-fashioned squirrel fur round her shoulders and carried what used to be called a raffia reticule as well as a handbag. Miss T...... was anything but smart; but there was a magnetism detectable in the strength of her face and eyes. Her voice, when she greeted the analyst, was deep and resonant. It would not have taken Sherlock Holmes to deduce that she had been trained as a singer.

"Dr de S......?" she inquired. "How nice of you to see me."

"Not at all. Do sit down. Here."

When he had dealt with the preliminaries—her name and date of birth, address and so on—his pen paused over the large blank space at the bottom of the white card headed "history".

"Now. Perhaps you would like to tell me something about your reasons for coming to see me. Let me see ..." he turned over a letter on his desk, scanning it. "Ah, yes. Dr W...... does say something here about your having undergone a long period of tension."

She looked at him suspiciously. "You mean to say you haven't heard of my—my trial?" she asked. "It was in all the papers."

"Tell me."

Dr de S......'s eyes were full on hers, bathing in their black pools. He had not answered her question, but it now needed no answer. She began to talk. At first her voice was muffled and stilted by embarrassment, but Dr de S......'s eyes stayed on her. In them, she found encouragement.

"It has all been like a terrible dream," she said. "I—I was accused of murdering another man's wife. Well. I wasn't guilty. *I* wasn't guilty. Not directly. But I can't stop blaming myself for Helen's death. I can't make myself believe that if I hadn't loved Jack as I did ..." she seemed to run out of words but it was as though her sentence continued in her brain. Dr de S...... waited. The desk light was on and the darkening room began to wrap his rotund visitor in chiaroscuro. He noticed that the ends of her fine hair were white.

"... Yes. I'm afraid I am altogether too passionate as a person. It does no good. Jack M...... was, I suppose you'd say, a perfectly happy man—married, two children finishing school, everything he wanted—when we were fated to meet. It was, well, hopeless from the word go."

Dr de S...... nodded understandingly. It was time now to interrupt. The Master would have allowed just this one dislocation.

"Perhaps," he said softly, "you would be more comfortable if you were to rest. While you tell me your story, I mean. Here ..."

He had moved round the desk and was gently leading her to the couch. He had the trick of melting into the background, so that it was only when he had settled her and turned on the light behind her head that she saw him clearly, as a person. By that time she was embarked on the continuation of her account.

"He was always terribly good to her," she said. "I have no way of knowing that what I am going to say is true. Yet I feel sure that he must have killed her. For my sake. And the thought is making it almost impossible for me to carry on. Is that frightfully weak? I suppose it is."

Dr de S....... did not reassure her. His whole concentration was on the way she was describing the events, and on the different emphases she was revealing in her affections for the *dramatis personae,* so to speak, of the case.

"Poor Helen. I never liked her much. She was always tidying him up so, making his life a quiet hell, in my opinion. They'd been married for donkeys' years, you see; it was one of those things that happen more often in the country than in town. They'd met practically as schoolchildren, fallen madly in love, and never gone out with anybody else in their lives. She was under seventeen, she once told me, when they first met. She'd had not one single other boy friend. Fantastic, isn't it?

"Anyway, my arrival was the straw that broke the camel in half! We met at a concert. I occasionally do masonics, when I'm not touring, and he was there. Very distinguished and charming in his evening dress. And something else as well. He was one of those well preserved Englishmen of middle years who have a deep twinkle in the back of their eyes. I fell for him, then and there."

Her eyes were staring up at the white ceiling. They were soft and round, like a young girl's.

"We were careful, of course. He thought the shock would do something terrible to her. We only met about twice a month, either when he had meetings or when I could manage a night in the hotel at Ringhurst. Then he'd motor over and we'd have dinner together. He used to tell her he was seeing one of his retired staff; and, to keep up appearances, he did usually drop in on one of them. Oh, we couldn't have been more careful. But country tongues wag, you know.

"I never did discover how Helen found out about us. It must have been one of her 'well-meaning' friends, I suppose. Probably she'd picked up a bit of tittle-tattle from the hotel, I don't know. Anyway, the first thing Jack knew was when she'd had a drink too many—she'd taken to it rather—and brazenly accused him of having a love affair with me. In front of a whole roomful of their friends. A pretty thing to do, I must say! But I don't blame her.

"I know how she must have felt, you see. There was—well, somebody else. Oh, years ago now. I've almost forgotten him. But *he* did it to *me*. I found her letters in his bag one night . . .

"Anyway, after that Helen wouldn't let him out of her sight. Jack had confessed the whole thing. He was utterly transparent. I've never known a man so lacking in any sort of guile. He just doesn't know the meaning of the word. So he owned up like a nice little English schoolboy and took his punishment. I believe he felt a sort of relief from all the deceit. Anyway, he rang me up from her bedroom while she sat there listening and told me he would never see me again.

"Of course, I got in touch with him as soon as possible. I knew Jack would never spurn me publicly like that. After what we had been to each other, it wasn't possible. I wrote him a note to his club, asking him to meet me for one final explanation, and he came. We had tea together.

"He was in an awful state, poor old duffer. More madly in love with me than ever before. I believe he'd have slaughtered a thousand savages for me on that afternoon. But he wouldn't leave her. Wouldn't dream of it. There was something perhaps Calvinistic in his make-up. He couldn't begin to see that there was a perfectly peaceful solution.

"We did not see each other again, after that, for nearly ten months. All the time she was watching him and taunting him. I know because he used to ring me up from a call box in the lane at the back of his house when he was desperate. Sometimes he was almost crying over the phone. I could hardly bear it.

"And I so well remember what he used to ask me. '*Must* I put up with it, Dorrie? *Must* I?' I didn't know what he meant by it when he said it. I didn't know what was in the back of his mind.

"Then we did meet. He said he had decided life was not worth living without me, so there it was. He did not say much, actually. I assumed he had cleared the path before arranging our rendezvous, but didn't bother to ask.

"All the time, she was lying dead in her little blue Mini Traveller, at the very end of a road they used to call "lovers' lane" quite near their house. He must have strangled her, I suppose, just before he came to see me."

She shuddered and covered her face with her hands in a convulsive gesture. "It was too horrible," she said. "How any man could do such a thing. *Even for love* . . ."

Her voice trailed off.

In a way it is a little sad to think how we often use love for others as a weapon. In the play *Lysistrata* by Aristophanes the girls refuse to go to bed with their husbands until they have abolished all war. Their intentions were certainly noble. But it happens often in daily life that we deprive each other of our love . . .

"An ABC of Love", Inge & Sten Hegeler

Chapter 14

5 p.m.

DANGER MEN

The factory hooters have blown time; girl office-workers are turning towards a thousand powder-rooms as though commanded by telepathy; shops hustling their last customers, beginning to bring things in from outside, to lock goods away; this is the last frayed stretch of the working rope around man's neck. Love's rush-hour.

"Coming to the pictures with me tonight?" *"Going skating?"* *"See you down the bowling alley?"* *"Will you be at the meeting?"* *"See you in the Bull, eh?"* *"I've got two tickets . . ."* These, and a multitude of other invitations, are on the air of evening. It is dating time for those who take their fences at a rush. It is also danger time, for those who are dated.

The boss has had time to digest his heavy lunch. The Beaujolais is no longer mulling his middle region. He is all afire, younger than his years, restless, randy. He is also coming nearer to the fatal hour when he must step into his Jaguar and sneak home through the traffic, to the cold supper and the even colder peck on the check from his lady wife. So what if his blood pressure isn't all that it was in the old days in the Eighth Army . . .

Burma . . . Berlin . . . the squadron . . . or what have you? He's still a damn sight fitter than he's given credit for. And, even if it does take a fairly discerning eye to see it these days, he *is* a fairly decent-looking chap who's looked after himself pretty well, all things considered. After all, it isn't so long ago that that young girl at the Christmas party latched on to him (much to his wife's contemptuous dismay). What he needs these days is *opportunity*. That is it. Take that new girl in the outer office, for instance . . .

Which is where the boss-fantasy grows dangerous. It is the work of a few seconds to press the obedient button, summon his discreet, faceless secretary (as attractive to him as cold tripe, but probably secretly, even subconsciously, in love with him in a way more mothers than flirting couples would understand), and demand on some pretext or another "send in that new girl . . . what's her name?"

He knows her name right enough. He noted much more than that at her interview. In fact, the only things about her he has overlooked since she joined the staff are small, carefully couched complaints about her untidiness, or dress, or general demeanour and—almost certainly—her unpunctuality, which have reached him through the faceless devotee.

When she comes, playing a heavily over-sophisticated role to hide her palpitating heart (because she is a woman, and has not been blind these last few weeks) he may fuss and hesitate, he most likely will pretend he wants her to work for him; to try her out; to give her a chance, or whatever other ruse enters his head; but the result will be the same. He'll end up with his arms round her, his hands moving on habitual routes, his lips seeking hers, the smell of his lunchtime brandy on his breath both attracting and revolting with its unfamiliarity, and the sharp stubble of his chin abrading her cheek under the hastily applied make-up.

Whether she goes or whether she doesn't, things are never going to be quite the same again for Miss New Girl after this encounter. It could be the Jaguar which takes her to the end of her street, long after the rest of the staff have gone and only the night watchman, or relief commissionaire, is there to turn a Nelsonic eye on their departure (the boss fussing about pretended work they had to do together; her insides quaking with the first nudge of fear). It could be the last bus. More likely, since this is still not a wholly libidinous isle and the sex appeal of an employer is not always enough to overcome the fact that he might be her father, or that he has never heard of Cathy McGowan, it will be the last journey she will make in the direction of the office.

But not all bosses are bad. And certainly not more than a tiny fraction of those for whom the gathering evening dark brings on the fantasy of clutching at one of the girls within easy reach ever moves a finger towards the button. Inhibition is often just laziness, and fear.

And shrieks like mandrakes torn out of the earth,
That living mortals, hearing them, run mad.
"Romeo and Juliet", Shakespeare

The evening plane out of Orly was less then half-filled with businessmen and others. Clive L...... was cheered up by the smile the B.O.A.C. hostess gave as he entered the cabin. He still had the pain in his chest which had started soon after he had left Yvette's apartment, and which refused to be banished by refreshment or alcohol. But the warmth and order of the plane made him forget for a moment his own wounded self-esteem.

He sat down and ordered cigarettes. When the girl brought them he asked if any interesting passengers were aboard. She said there were several important people flying home from the exhibition, but nobody actually famous. She leaned lightly on the arm of the seat in front of him to talk to him. Everyone else seemed to be aboard and the hostess looked at her watch.

At the last minute a tanned, loose-skinned man in his early fifties came and sat in one of the two empty seats across the aisle from Clive. He nodded, panting slightly from the exertion. The next few minutes were taken up with the procedure of becoming air-borne, then as they slipped the buckles free from their seat belts, the newcomer leaned over and spoke.

"Glad to get out of it, aren't you?" he asked.

Clive looked at him, surprised. "Not especially," he said. "I'm rather partial . . ."

The older man cut him short. He had lifted himself out of his seat and plumped himself down beside Clive, obviously set on continuing the discussion at close quarters.

"They hate us, of course," he said. "That's behind it all, if you think about it."

Clive decided to be tactful. "I expect it takes all sorts," he said. "What about a drink?"

"I could do with a whole bottle," said the man beside him. "But, thanks, I'll settle for a whisky and soda. With relish as a matter of fact. I'm sure the stuff they were selling me as scotch had never seen a bank or a brae in its life."

109

Clive leaned up and pressed the button above his head, illuminating a small electric light over his seat and summoning the stewardess. She came along almost immediately.

"Two whiskies. Soda, please," said Clive. Then to the man beside him: "Ice?"

"Most definitely not," said the man.

When the young woman had gone, smiling at this staunch Anglicism, he struggled with his collar and tie which seemed to be causing him discomfort though they were soft and loose. For a moment Clive felt panic at the notion that he might be closeted with some lunatic. Then his companion spoke again.

"You've no idea what I've been through," he said. "Savages. Bloody primitives."

Clive felt it was better to leave the matter there. His companion was plainly lost in thoughts so bitter and disturbing that he had ceased to be aware of him. He went on talking.

"I made a fatal mistake," he said, "in taking her at her face value. Bah! She and her entire family weren't worth my little finger. And the wretches had the bare-faced audacity to question *my* family background!"

The hum of the intercom cut in and for the next few moments they were distracted by the captain's announcement of their whereabouts, expected time of arrival in London and weather details. When it was finished, the man said abruptly:

"Mustn't let me bore you with my worries, old man. Sorry I spoke."

Clive had had time to weigh up his travelling companion. The man might be a bore but he was not a looney. Something about him began to interest Clive.

"Carry on," he said. "Does one good to let rip occasionally."

The man looked at him with tired, unhappy eyes. "I've had the lot of them," he said. "I don't want to meet another frog as long as I live. Not one."

"You sound bitter."

"I am. I've been a bloody fool. You wouldn't think I was fifty-four would you?" Clive waggled his head politely. "Well, I am. And I'm still capable of making a damned idiot of myself over a woman."

"Aren't we all?" asked Clive feelingly.

"At my age, it hurts," said the man. "Here." He thumped his chest over his heart. "But she was such a bad one, you've no idea. You couldn't have. See this . . ." he leaned forward, parting the grizzled hair on his skull to display a long, livid scar. "That was where she cracked me over the nut with a champagne bottle."

"Were you married to this lady?"

"Married to her? I'll say I wasn't. We were engaged, it's true, but it would have taken a firing squad to get me to the altar alongside her. No, 'this lady' as you call her was my fiancée. I met her in England in rather curious circumstances."

"Oh?"

"Yes. I don't suppose many fellows advertise for a wife. I did. When my wife died I put an advertisement in the paper for a woman who would share my house. It was big, you know: twelve rooms. And I hated being alone in it."

"What happened?"

"Well, nothing except that I could hardly get out of my door for letters, all from females wanting the job. I had said something in the advert about 'sharing every pleasurable amenity'. That brought them in droves."

He took a long pull at his whisky which the girl had brought and quietly put before them on the hinged seat trays.

"Yes. I had a dickens of a job choosing out of that lot, I can tell you. I almost decided to start a harem." He chuckled.

"Is that where you found your fiancée?"

"Yes. I was a damn fool, I suppose. She was only twenty-one, you see. I should have known better. But the letter she wrote was just the thing. Said she was a student and an orphan and had always wanted to care for a man who wasn't just a silly youngster her own age. She actually tried to pretend, in that letter, now I look back on it, that she was the serious, soulful type."

"Well, wasn't she?"

"Wasn't she, hell! That girl is no more interested in the serious things of life than you are in jumping out of this aeroplane. Except money. Oh, she's seriously interested in money right enough. And so are her sisters and her cousins and her aunts. And that ferocious old hen of a mother of hers. But I hadn't met them, of course. She kept them from me until the last possible moment."

"Is that what you've been in Paris for? To meet your fiancée's parents?" Clive was feeling much brighter.

"My *ex*-fiancée's parents. I met them. All. What a bunch! I'd sooner be shut up in a cage with a pack of hyenas."

"So you're not going to marry her?"

"I certainly am not. Tell me—you look like a bit of a man of the world— would *you* tolerate a girl who spends two hours in the

111

bathroom before you can even take her outside for a cup of tea? That's what this pretty young missy did."

"Sounds pretty long, I must say."

"It was nothing to what she could do when she tried. Every time I asked her out—along came the 'fam-eee'. And *eat*? They couldn't have had a square meal, any of them, for a month before I came over.

"They've been eating about twenty quid's worth of food a day between them, ever since I got over to this benighted city. And all at my expense!"

He finished his drink and banged down the glass. "Well. That's the lot, as far as I'm concerned. Never again. It's a bachelor's life for me. A widower's rather. I suppose if I hadn't told her about the money my wife left me . . . Ah, but what's the good of wondering. Have another drink?"

"Thanks."

"I don't suppose you would do a damn silly thing like that would you?"

"Hmm. We're all fools when it comes to women, aren't we?"

"Aye," said the man trenchantly. "We are that. Only some of us are bigger damn fools than the others. Two more scotches please miss."

How many lovers have there been who have looked into a husband's eyes and asked themselves, "which of us is deceiving the other?"

. . . there is no good ending to a love affair. It may end dramatically, bitterly or even hilariously. It does not end satisfactorily.

"The Winning Art", David Malcolm (*Max Parrish*)

Chapter 15

6 p.m.

DANGER WOMEN

In the dark, a young slip of a girl walks up the damp length of Whitfield Street, where the warmth of Soho has become the industrial east of the Tottenham Court Road. At 106 she pauses, rings and is allowed to enter. Her mission, at this late hour, is one which all England should know to its shame.

For this girl is an unmarried mother. She is deeply, seriously and—as far as can be surmised—likely to remain in love with the young student she calls her "sweetheart". They have been engaged to be married for eighteen months, and lovers for nearly two years. The baby they have had is now being adopted. The girl is coming here, to the merciful Marie Stopes Centre and Clinic, for "advice", as she would put it. More clinically, she is coming to be "fitted up".

Where else could she go?

Britain in the sixties may toy with the idea of being emancipated, may shun the old Victorian ways of forcing women to suffer "for their sins". But it has a coldness at its heart which sees danger in giving birth control—contraceptives—to young girls.

For fear of promiscuity.

Well, the statistics are certainly on its side. Earnest—and prurient—researchers have produced articles for Sunday newspapers to show the galloping downhill slide of morals and sexual decency.

These have, it is true, recently been kicked in their clichés by a scholarly social psychologist from Cambridge University. Michael Schofield's survey showed another side of the coin.

But sexual delinquency remains the bane of parents, the worry of magistrates and the besetting interest of all self-appointed moral policemen.

In Whitfield Street, we can hear a refreshing view on all this: "Statistics," says Dr Faith Spicer, "are almost never reliable. There has *always* been a pool of promiscuous girls in this country; it is no worse now than ever it was. And promiscuity does not, as some people seem to think, necessarily stem from ill-health, either physical or mental. This, I feel sure."

At six in the evening, as Cupid goes to work, we may thank heaven for such a practical view. Dr Spicer is not a moral guardian. She does not look like one. She is blue-eyed and fair-haired, tall and slim. Her humorous mouth, personal neatness and pleasant voice add up to a most attractive personality. Women, especially younger women with problems on their minds, feel when with her as though they have suddenly met a close personal friend.

She and her colleagues at Whitfield Street do noble work. Without them, I estimate that the number of suicides among young London women would rise well above its present total—whether one credits statistics or not.

Those who come to them have sometimes tried hard elsewhere, without success. Nobody wants to help the unmarried mother prevent her family growing at nature's will. Nobody really wants to help the schoolgirl lover at all.

"They come here for birth control," Dr Spicer says. "And they almost invariably ask for advice afterwards."

So the Marie Stopes Clinic is more than a clinic for fitting dutch caps and inter-uterine devices. It is a place where women in trouble can come and talk to sympathetic, intelligent people.

In a recent year, Dr Spicer and the others saw 564 new cases. There were three girls among them who listed their occupation as "schoolgirl".

Out of these anxious women, 263 were under 21 years old.

Some wrote before they came; a typical letter reads something like this:

"I am twenty-two and engaged to a boy I love very much, but we both want to get established in our careers before tying ourselves down to marriage. We have had a child which is now being adopted, as neither of us is financially well off at present.

"The authorities don't seem interested in helping us unless we get married first.

"I went to a doctor. She said she would help. She charged me £3, just for a chat. She did not solve the problem at all.

"As I am very much in love with my sweetheart, I am terrified it will happen again. I just don't feel I can wait the two and a half years before we finish our training and can marry.

"Could you help us?"

Dr Faith Spicer and her colleagues can and will. Such women in trouble have only to ask.

Ted S...... might never have gone to Blackpool if his mother had not taunted him about his new suit. It was a summery affair, in pale-blue dressed linen and he wore it with a darkly striped shirt and plain knitted-silk tie. He had felt just the thing in it, but Mrs......, when she had first seen it at breakfast, had exclaimed in a shocked tone of voice: "Whatever did you go and buy a thing like that for, Ted?"

Ted was embarrassed. He could well afford the suit and several like it. What was wrong with buying a suit of clothes he fancied? He worked hard enough for the money. People talked about overtime as if all you had to do was go in a pick up the "double-bubble" at the end of it. It wasn't like that at all.

He ate his fried egg in silence, deciding on a plan. He'd been uneasy with his mother ever since coming home this time. It was only for a week. But why should he waste it sitting at home if he wasn't wanted? Him and his suit.

"I'll be going to Blackpool for the day, ma," he announced as he sipped his second cup of tea. He'd made his plan. Why not? He had the money to spend a day on the spree. If they didn't like the way he dressed himself down here in Wormsleycott, he'd soon find somebody who would appreciate him up there.

He knew Blackpool, vaguely, from holiday visits with his folks. And from outings. But he had never been there in winter and the thought stimulated him.

Perhaps he'd find a bit of stuff, free for the day, like. He thought about the prospect in the train. As he sauntered away from the station towards the front and the Golden Mile, it was still in his mind.

The only girls about were either pushing prams or carrying laden shopping baskets. Most of them were wearing scarves or shawls over their hair, against the cold wind. He felt depressed. He walked across the road to a cafe with condensed moisture running down the inside of the windows and steam coming from a vent. There were lights inside and the dim shapes of people. It offered a sort of welcome.

The girl, when he first saw her, was talking to two men. They must have finished their teas and departed while he was ordering and being served, because when he looked round again she was alone. She was taking a cigarette from a packet and lighting it so that the flame of her lighter illuminated the carefully-painted, pale-mauve curve of her lips and the even tone of her made-up face.

She was blonde. Peroxide, he said to himself with worldly understanding. Her eyes were exaggerated with a frame of dark pencil, but even without they were surprisingly wide. She wore long, heavily-blackened lashes.

Ted saw that her figure was O.K. She was slim and the shortness of her white, unbelted mack showed legs which, even in the curious disguise of dark embroidered stockings, were enticingly shaped.

Hmm, thought Ted appreciatively. I wonder...

He moved over to the girl, taking a cigarette out of his own packet. "Would you mind?" he asked. Their eyes met. She flicked the lighter and held it out for him"

"Where do you get those, then?" she asked. His cigarette came from a brown packet of *Sweet Afton* which a fellow at the works had sold him cheap because he didn't fancy them. "Are you over from Ireland?"

"Thanks. No, I'm from quite close to here. Just spending a short time here to see the sights, like. You know."

"Oh, aye. But where's the sights, then, at this time of year?"

"Well," he said with great daring. "You're one of them."

She opened her narrow eyes as wide as they would go. "Aye, aye!" she said. "Listen to Romeo, then. I'll bet you say that to all the girls."

They giggled in harmony and he moved closer. "Like something to eat?" he asked softly, his eyes on hers. "I wouldn't mind," she told him.

They sat at a small table under the wireless, which was tuned to a pirate station and blaring out barely-interrupted pop. By the time the beans on toast were ready he knew her name: Lee.

She was between jobs, she told him. Not hurried or worried. Plenty more where they came from. She had a nice room, not too far from the front. And in summer there were always plenty of jobs to be picked up.

He asked if she would like to spend the day with him and she pretended to consider the enormity of his proposal; as though she was prepared to turn him down. But she came with him when they left the cafe, though she had not actually accepted.

What was left of the morning, they spent in a cinema. She let him hold her hand, then slide his arm round her, in the empty dark. Only about a dozen other people were in the hall with them.

She put her cheek against his and their lips met in what was, to him, an exciting kiss. Her lips were thin and she pushed him away, but he felt elated at his conquest. In the interval she excused herself and went to the Ladies. When she came back she smelt strongly of face-powder.

They had coffee and cakes for lunch, and he ate a pork pie. They smoked a lot of cigarettes. Then they decided to look for a few of the entertainments which were open out-of-season.

Looking back, he had enjoyed those two hours with her the best. He spent his money on the dodgems with wild abandon, and they just kept riding round and round, nudging the barrier and the parked cars. They were seldom accompanied by more than one or two members of the public. In the jolting car, he managed to get his hand on her knee and she made no strong effort to make him take it away.

She seemed to be enjoying herself. It was hard to believe what happened afterwards.

She had suggested a walk on the wind-blown sands after tea. It was dark and they had to pick their way down the steps from the promenade. Exhilarated, he pretended to run ahead of her so that she had difficulty in seeing and catching up with him. Then he came back and put his arm round her.

Just after six-thirty, he asked if she had had enough by now. Would she like to go back to a pub? She persuaded him to stay a while longer. She knew a place, she said, where it was quite sheltered. He chuckled coarsely, saying he'd bet she did. Been there with others, he supposed?

Something told him they weren't alone on the beach, in the darkness, but he took no notice. In the fold of a dune they lay down side by side on his mac. He had his hand inside her blouse

117

and his knee pressing to separate her legs when the four men came up to them.

One, the one in front, caught hold of Ted's jacket collar and yanked him backwards so that he fell crab-like on the sand. The others kicked him. When he managed to get to his feet, the smallest of the four hit him over his eyes with a hard glass object which might have been a Coca-Cola bottle. Before he lost consciousness, he saw the girl with her arm round one of the boys' waists.

When he came to, he was lying on the dune. His mouth was full of blood and sand. His pockets were empty of everything. More than thirty-five quid holiday money was gone. And his Parker pen.

He spat out the filth in his mouth; felt his teeth which, though sore, were still in place as far as he could tell. He pulled himself painfully to his feet.

The new suit was a crumpled, blood-bespattered mess.

True love makes the thought of death frequent, easy, without terrors; it becomes merely a standard of comparison, the price one would pay for many things.

"Maxims of Love", Stendhal (*Merlin Press*)

Chapter 16

7 p.m.

ALL CHANGE

As night closes in, we might care to consider where *we* stand in all this. It is to be noted that during the Middle Ages fornication was a more serious crime than manslaughter. An authority, writing on sex and English law, gives it as a considered opinion that "The English, of course, love to believe that ... English morality is, after all, the fairest and most decent code of living that the world has yet produced. The case-books of psychiatrists and the records of the courts suggest that such complacency may be out of place..."

What do we know or care about such mores and attitudes? Our behaviour is largely instinctive. The bunch of young clerical juniors from a City insurance office now probing the depths of London's West End are not restrained by moral compunction. Their doubts are material. *Will it be worth it? Can they afford the price?* They are in the grip of a stronger emotion than moral diffidence. As Mr G. Rattray Taylor has reminded us in his book *Sex in History* (Thames and Hudson, 1953):

"It is tempting to speculate whether some important change of personality may not be occurring in Britain ... If so, it will certainly have its effect on sexual relations and since it is a form of immaturity, it will hardly be a desirable one ..."

It can certainly be said that there are symptoms of distortion noticeable, as the chimes of Big Ben toll the seventh hour of evening; and as Dr de S..... prepares to leave for a lecture, having spent a fruitless hour at his desk waiting for Margie B......

The bell rang as he was slipping some papers into a thin leather dispatch case. He zipped it shut, clicked his tongue irritably and went out into the hall. "Vivienne?" he called sharply. There was no reply. Dr de S...... opened the front door.

His old medical-school friend Ian F..... was on the doorstep. A young, pretty girl with a pale face and thin, fair hair stood beside him, rubbing her shoes on the mat. He sensed the girl's nervousness and deliberately ignored her.

"Come in, Ian," he said in a low, warm voice. "I was expecting you earlier."

Dr F...... was not totally at ease in the sophisticated ambience of Julian de S...... 's hallway. "I'm most dreadfully sorry, Julian," he said, shaking hands. "We had the dickens of a drive up. Traffic's appalling. Anyway, here we are; and I hope you can spare us a few minutes."

Dr de S...... took his coat and put it on a chair. He preferred to see outdoor garments put neatly away in the vestibule, but there was no time now for such details. *Where was Vivienne?* He smiled:

"I have to go on to one of these boring meetings," he said, "As a matter of fact I was just on the point of leaving. But it can wait a while, quite happily. They won't miss me. Come in, do."

When the panelled mahogany door was closed, and they were seated, Dr F...... explained as briefly as possible how he had met Margie in the train; how she had confided in him. While he was doing this, she sat looking fixedly at Dr de S..... with wide, frightened eyes.

"I see," said the analyst calmly, making a small note on a pad in front of him. For the first time since their arrival he turned his eyes towards her. "Well," he said easily, "why don't we have a little talk and I'll see how we can help you? If Dr F...... will excuse us; just for a little while......"

His voice, she decided, was like a coo-ing dove. Hearing him address her, she felt wonderfully restored and uplifted. When the other doctor had gone, she let him lead her to the couch. She climbed easily on to it. The comfort made her drowsy and she soon forgot the instinctive feeling she had that it was rather daft to be lying down in this room.

She told him all about her affair with Ron. All about her mother, and their cottage. And all about Miss Evans, too, and the school homework. Her story, hardly prompted, took under ten minutes.

"And the thought of having this baby frightens you, doesn't it?" he asked afterwards. He was sitting beside her, making notes as she spoke. It made her feel rather important and light-headed.

"Well, yes," she said in a small voice.

"It shouldn't, Margie," he said.

The over forty-fives are the age group with the highest proportion of disapprovers of birth control, but this is only 13 per cent. This is also the age group that, more than any other, thinks sex relations should be solely for the purpose of having children.

From "Television & Religion", A report by Social Surveys (Gallup Poll) Ltd. on behalf of ABC Television

It was his third double whisky and the barman in the Railway Hotel looked at him suspiciously as he ordered it. While he waited for the drink, he pretended to read his evening paper. "Russian moon pictures a fake," he read. His thoughts drifted and he no longer saw the printed front page in front of him. When the drink came, he paid for it with a pound note and pocketed the change. Mentally, he was three years back, seeing the way it had all started with Mary. Even as the whisky swilled to the back of his mouth, he felt the acrid bitterness of his misery. Why, why, why had he been such a simpleton? he asked himself.

Or was Mary right? He wasn't good with figures, or anything to do with money and business and that sort of thing. Whenever he had to make a decision he found himself in a blue funk, even if nobody could suffer from it but himself. She had seen this and said she was doing it to help him.

Let's see, how had she put it: "You're not to worry yourself over these things, Bert. Leave them to me. You've got me now, haven't you?" That was the trouble, he most certainly had. Oh how he wished he hadn't.

What had ever possessed him to answer that advertisement in the *Advertiser* when she'd put it in? Loneliness, he supposed. After Vi had left him, there had been some terrible moments of emptiness in his life. The advert had read alluringly, "Lady of mature age interested in meeting a single gentleman with a view to marriage. Widowers, divorcees or others in lonely situations perfectly acceptable."

When he wrote, he put down a lot about Vi and the children. It had been a relief somehow to get it off his chest. For a couple of days he had gone round with nothing much else in his mind but the impatience to receive an answer and the wonder over what it would be. He began taking an interest in his appearance, and bought a new pale blue shirt. He had his iron-grey hair trimmed. At sixty-one he was still a handsome man.

Mary's reply was almost tersely non-committal. If interested further, would the gentleman please meet the undersigned outside the front entrance of Swan and Edgar's, Piccadilly Circus, on such and such a night at 7 o'clock. And would he, for the purposes of identification, please be carrying a copy of the *Advertiser*..."

Herbert A......was there five minutes ahead of time. He felt shabby in his six-year-old overcoat, though it had hardly been worn. He had shaved a second time before coming out from Wandsworth. He looked at his watch and counted the seconds until she came.

He felt no disappointment when she came up to him. She was not beautiful, but there was a firm strength about her face which appealed to him. His own family had always had weak lines. He had been teased at school about his lack of chin. The hint of masculinity in Mary S...... was encouraging.

They went to Lyons and had a meal. At first, their talk was strictly on generalities. It was hard to believe they had met as they had, for the stated purpose of marrying if it suited them to do so. She was the first to broach the subject, as she poured his second cup of tea and passed it across.

"I suppose, Mr A......" she said rather tautly, "you will have given some thought to what I put in my advertisement?"

His heart jumped and pounded. "Oh, yes, Mrs S......", he assured her. "I most certainly have. You see, my wife..."

"Passed away?" she asked helpfully.

"No. No, she left me. I don't know why. She took the children after school and just went away. I wasn't able to trace them. All I have had in ten years was a card saying they were all right, posted in Broadstairs. That's why I divorced her."

"I see." Mrs S......'s dark eyes were almost luminous with concentration. "May I ask a personal question, Mr A......?" she said.

122

"Of course."

"Then did you love your wife?"

"I . . . I'm not sure. At first, I must have done, mustn't I? But I suppose I took her for granted after a few years."

She had left it at that with what he thought was commendable tact. They met six times in all before he asked her back to Wandsworth to see the house. She was obviously impressed, as he had intended that she should be.

Her own husband, she told him, had been killed in a street accident when only forty-five. She had brought up a daughter and a son, both now married and living away from home. She was lonely. She saw no reason for living out her life, as she put it, "like a field-mouse shut away in a barn". She wanted to settle down, with a respectable man, and enjoy her declining years with him.

The house visit seemed to have clinched it with Mary. From then on she talked always of "when" rather than "if". They both became quite coy and enthusiastic over plans for their marriage. It was quietly, quickly and almost clinically done at a Registry Office and they spent a fortnight at Bognor Regis afterwards, staying in a hotel.

She had insisted on twin beds. He understood that she did not intend to enter into the physical side of their contract. On all other matters, however, she became almost pressingly interested in his affairs. The deeds of the house, when he showed them to her, were promptly stuffed away in her handbag on the excuse that she would study them later (though, as far as he knew, no reason existed for her studying them at all). He did not like to argue with her, or to show any sign of mistrust. So he allowed small happenings like these to proceed unchecked.

It was when she asked him about his will that he first became uneasy. She was so insistent. In the finish he had to tell her that he had left everything to Vi, for the children's sake. She appeared to be horrified.

For painful hours afterwards, she took him to task for what she called his "private weakness" towards the woman who had deserted him. She tried to make him see that Vi was worthless. That he was behaving weakly and stupidly in letting her benefit from his death. In the end, he gave in.

He produced the will for her to "study" and she promptly tore it up and threw it on the fire. "There," she said, holding the burning paper over the coals with the poker, "now she won't get her hands on your money. I hope she rots for what she has done to you."

The same afternoon she told him she was making her own will entirely in his favour, ignoring her own children. The inference was too obvious to miss. He obediently had his will re-drawn by his solicitor in London so that she became the sole beneficiary. The night he brought it home, she had prepared his favourite supper. He handed her the folded, stiff paper document and she put it away in her handbag, as she had done the deeds.

"I'll see it's safe," she said.

It had been a slow process ever since. First, her complaints about the way he kept the house. Remarks of hers, pointing to comparison between Herbert and the neighbours, who seemed to spend all their weekends in shirt-sleeves working at odd jobs. Herbert was a man who lacked confidence in his ability to use tools. He invariably, by habit and instinct, shirked such household duties until the last possible moment.

In consequence, Mary's irritability soon became anger. She had a sharp tongue when upset. She used it on Herbert with devastating effect. He began to fear returning to the house. And when she finally told him, during a paroxysm of rage, that he was a "parasite" in her house, and that if he wanted to be merely a boarder then he'd better pay her rent as one, he agreed immediately.

It had seemed a reasonable way out at the time. Provided he paid her £3 a week, she said, he might stay in peace as far as she was concerned. She would pay a man, with the emphasis on the word *man*, to come in and do the necessary jobs for him.

But this haven was short-lived also. He found her increasingly bad-tempered and edgy. Nothing he could do or say seemed to please her. They had moved into separate rooms and Herbert lay in a draughty attic between an ill-fitting door and a loose window under the eaves of the old house. As a result, he developed a cold which went to his chest. The cough refused to go and at night he sometimes found it impossible not to give it vent. She seemed to lie awake in the master bedroom below waiting for him to cough so that she could thump on the ceiling with her stick.

He had begun to lose weight. His work was a labour such as he had never before endured, and the gentleman he clerked for had scolded him several times lately for wrong entries and untidy, slipshod work. Tonight, he had come to the end of the road. He was determined to have it out with her. She was a good soul, he was sure of that. If he talked to her, he could make her see sense, perhaps.

But another side of his brain told him he hated her. The whisky he had taken to give himself courage for the approaching interview seemed to have unveiled hostilities in him which had lain unsuspected in his brain for the whole of his lifetime. On an impulse, he asked the barman for a threepenny piece and went to the coin box in the corner, dialling his number.

Mary's voice came through, saying something he did not distinguish, and he pushed in the coin quickly. For a few seconds, the bleeps shut away her voice and he had time to wonder why she had seemed to be in conversation. Then he was through.

Before he could speak, he realized that it *was* Mary's voice. She was speaking to someone else, on another line. He must have cut into their call, through some fault in the system. He put his hand over the mouthpiece and listened.

". . . up to you," she was saying. "Why don't you carry a copy of the paper? I'll look out for it."

A man's voice answered. He sounded quiet, respectable and elderly. "Yes," he said. "Yes, I'll do that. And I'll see you at seven o'clock, as arranged, just outside Swan and Edgar's main entrance. I know where you mean.

"Goodbye, then," she said.

"Goodbye," he replied. "I'll see you on Thursday."

Herbert waited for the clicks and the dial tone before gently replacing his receiver. The fates, he mused, had been kind to Herbert A. . . . . . this night. He went slowly over to the bar and asked for a large whisky and another threepenny piece. When the drink came he told the barman, gratuitously: "I want to phone my solicitor."

The man only nodded, but Herbert smiled. He was thinking of Mary's haughty face when he and his solicitor would confront her, and the man who had answered her advertisement, at seven o'clock on Thursday evening.

Chapter 17

8 p.m.

SWINGING

In the large sitting-out area of the Café de Paris in London a Cupid-conscious management has provided low lighting. Here, hands are entwining, glances communicating promises. On the tiny subterranean dance floor of ffinches at Eastbourne, a girl with Joan Baez hair and eyes strokes the face of the lanky boy she is dancing in front of. The pattern is similar all over Britain. Restaurants, cinemas, dancehalls, bowling alleys, skating rinks, theatres, parks . . . they are the eight o'clock background to the drama of boy meets girl. What else?

Detective-Sergeant Hubert L. . . . . . is in bed with the kinky prostitute at her flat while the man he arrested with her (whom, she protests, is *not* her husband) sits in his cell at Mr L. . . . . .'s place of work. It turns out that the detective has met her before. They are old friends. This is by way of a reunion.

Dr de S. . . . . . is excusing himself for being late at the meeting of the Promotion of Oral Contraceptive Society (P.O.C.S.) while making a mental resolution to ring his intellectual mistress, Inge,

126

in Hampstead so that he can catch her before she goes out to eat, and thus arrange a little relaxation; after all, he has had a busy day and there is still no sign of Vivienne.

Vivienne de S. . . . . is in Maida Vale, holding hands with two women, one on either side of her, while they invoke the spirit world. Her eyes are shut and she appears to be in a state of cataleptic fervour as her mouth forms the simple syllable "Jim". She is remembering the boy with a tuft of gold-blond hair under his school cap who used to carry her satchel up the hill.

Margie B. . . . . . is watching the windscreen wipers of Dr F. . . . . .'s car polish and re-polish the hemispheres of clear glass as they drive through Staines. He, in the driving seat, is silent, contemplating ways and means for her to be admitted to the hospital where he is a consultant. On an impulse he asks her: "I suppose there's no chance of you both marrying later on, and wanting to have the child back?" Margie answers: "I'd never thought of that."

Maureen J. . . . . . and Gerald A. . . . . ., the couple we met early this morning when the postman disturbed their slumbers and brought the cruise tickets, are eating gnocchi in a Chelsea *bistro*, arguing over whether it would be better to change to the Express Dairy who deliver on Sundays.

The young man who kissed Sally in the lift, and had a most embarrassing time subsequently, narrowly missing being arrested and having to apologize to a furious woman who now seemed as little attractive to him as his own sister, is in the Blue Boar; tipsy, telling a group of young men in white collars and the modern equivalent of the pin-stripe suit how he swept her off her feet.

Panoramically, lovers do not seem very different in Britain to elsewhere. There are exceptions, however.

"It is quite understandable she hadn't had any experience, but *fantastic* nobody should have told her *anything*," he said.

Marcia nodded. "That's the trouble with the world today." She spoke with a pronounced lisp. "It's full of enforced ignorance."

He passed his cup over and she took it, automatically lifting the cosy off the coffee-pot with her other hand. "She'll be here in a minute," he said, hearing the eight o'clock pips interrupt the Third Programme on the wireless in the lounge.

"Yes. Why don't you tell her all she ought to know, Conrad? I mean, she'll not get it straight in her mind from what we were saying to her on Tuesday, will she?"

"I'd better, I suppose. She's a nice kid. It's not her fault she's practically a grown woman and still mentally a babe in arms. You remember what Shaw said?"

"Of course. It's all in Kafka, too. What I feel so dreadfully is that she'll probably . . . I mean after you've taken all this trouble with her, Conrad . . . fall for some frightful moron. It'll all be wasted, I mean."

"Well." He was leafing through a copy of *New Society*, angrily. "How can they just *ignore* books," he muttered. "Yes, well, that's it, isn't it? I mean, sweety-pie, if she needs educating at her age—what is she, rising thirteen—it just shows the true state of what is laughingly called British education."

There was a pause. She was listening to Greek dirges being played on original 350 B.C. instruments by students from the Hellespont University. He was reading.

The bell rang.

"There she is. I'll leave you together in here while I get dressed. I suppose I'd better have a bath, if the geyser is working." She sounded unenthusiastic.

"Here," he said. He passed her a shilling. "It's sure to need it. Take as long as you like. Wallow in it." He stood up. "I've decided something." he said.

"What?"

"I'm going to *show* her. In practice, I mean. An actual demonstration."

"You mean . . ."

"Exactly. Intercourse, and all that. Do you object, I mean?"

"Well. I suppose, in the interests of science . . ."

"Rational science!"

"Of course. Rational science. As I say, in that case, I suppose . . . Well, I suppose, no. I don't object. Go ahead." Her voice was beginning to sound shrill. "Yes, I think it's an absolutely fabulous idea," she ended lamely.

"Good. Well, you'd better let her in, hadn't you. Thank God Sebastien's quiet for the moment."

She went out into the narrow hall smelling of dank copper from the collection of old musical instruments hanging on its dingy walls. The door had glass panes which rattled as she tugged it open against the jamb where the rain had swollen it.

"Hallo," she said. "Come in and take off your ghastly wet things."

The girl was like a small field animal. She more or less bounced into the hallway, flicking droplets from a small umbrella and

128

slipping out of a camel hair coat which might have been the skin of a vole. She was breathless.

"I caught the bus to the memorial," she said. "But I ran all the way here. It was silly, but I thought somebody was following me."

"Come in. Conrad is reading."

In the light, without the coat and headscarf which she had also discarded, the girl was dazzlingly beautiful. She had dark, curling hair and almost violet eyes fringed with the darkest lashes imaginable. Her figure, though as yet unformed fully, was already alluring.

"Is he asleep?"

"Sebastien? Yes, thank God. He was almost asleep in his bath, he was so tired. We had some people here last night and I rather forgot about him, so he didn't get to bed until after ten."

The girl smiled. "I'll go up and see he's all right, later on," she said.

She put her outdoor clothes over a chair and walked on into the living room. Marcia went upstairs, deliberately leaving them together. Then curiosity overcame her. She tiptoed back down the stairs and into the passage, after only five or six minutes.

Conrad's voice, distorted to a drone through the closed door, told her where he had got to in his instructive discourse. ". . . feel it, you see, like that," he was saying.

There was a pause, then the girl spoke, somewhat huskily.

"Yes. Now."

"Well, that is how it is; all over. Havelock Ellis first discovered the regions, you know. He used a strand of silk. Drew it backward and forwards. and counted the number of times. He located all the erogenous areas, isolated them and compared their reactive qualities. Fascinating."

"Yes. I've never thought of it before. You mean . . ."

"Look, I'll show you."

Another silence ensued. Marcia shuddered slightly and went quietly upstairs.

Kissing is a form of sexual contact acceptable by most people even in semi-public places, but most other kinds of love-making usually take place in private. Furthermore they are subject to more restrictions, limitations and taboos, and can only take place when the circumstances are expedient.

"The Sexual Behaviour of Young People",
Michael Schofield

"Talking of baths," said Clarissa, "whose turn is it? Because if nobody else wants it, I do."

Seven of the ten unmarried girls living at Westchester House sat in various attitudes of relaxed ease round the T.V. set in the lounge of Captain T. . . . . .'s residence for young ladies, known locally as "the henhouse". As well as Clarissa, there was Georgina, Millie, Fiona, Drusilla, Caroline and Gwenda. Three were secretaries, two receptionists, one an advertising copy-writer, and Clarissa was a T.V. production assistant.

Nobody spoke. Clarissa stuck her needles firmly into the jumper she was halfway through, jerked herself out of the sofa and made for the door. "Anyone got a sixpence?" she asked.

"Sorry." "No." "Not a hope." "Ask the Captain."

"Hell."

Clarissa walked out into the cream-painted hallway and tapped at a door marked *Office*. A gruff voice called "Come in," and she entered.

"Oh, Captain T. . . . . ., could you *please* let me have a sixpence for the gas meter, if I absolutely *promise* to give it back to you tomorrow enening?"

"Going to have a bath? Make yourself nice and fresh?" The landlord's accent was a combination of Wellington College, Woolwich, too much pipe-smoking and thirty years in Paddington. "I don't know why you blessed girls don't keep a hoard of sixpences, 'pon my soul," he grumbled.

She giggled nervously, accepting the coin he handed her from a tin petty-cash box. "I know, we're dreadful," she said. "But thank you *so* much; you're a dear."

"Hmm."

She went out and climbed the stairs to her room on the second floor. As soon as she had gone, the Captain opened his office door a few inches and sat listening. When he heard Clarissa's door open and close for the second time, followed by the noise of water running into the bath, he went outside and quietly climbed the stairs to his own room.

Captain John T. . . . . . was a bachelor. A bit of a gay dog, the girls understood. They had strong, laid-down house-rules about not encouraging him, or allowing him the slightest licence with any of them. A form of protective shorthand passed between them, understood by all. In their book, he was someone to be treated with enormous politeness and held at arm's length, rather like a pet python.

None of them had ever seen inside his room. It was sparsely

130

furnished, but with two large ornately framed paintings of beautiful woman of the French court, painted by Fragonard. When his father had died, he had sold up everything except these two pictures.

He came in now, barely giving them a glance. When he had shut the door behind him, he went over to a well-worn armchair under the window and sat down. He took off his shoes and replaced them with woollen, soft-soled slippers. Then he took off his jacket and put on a maroon, padded-silk smoking jacket.

He got to his feet. In the corner of the room was a large, built-in cupboard. He opened the door of this, pushed aside some suits of clothes hanging from a central rail and, with a hooked stick which was standing in the corner, opened a trapdoor in the ceiling. It exposed the loft.

A hinged, collapsible ladder came down to his feet. He climbed into the space above. This was floored over. Two tanks, one large and one small, stood on wooden trestles. From one of these came the hissing sound of water running down to the bathroom below.

The Captain moved over to a space under the eaves of the old house where he was directly over the bathroom. From here, the sound of the geyser and of someone moving about were quite distinct. He lay full length and put his eye to a small pane of blackened glass.

Like a two-way mirror, the peephole allowed someone in the loft to see into the bathroom without being seen. A large mirror had been placed on one of the walls, in a position which revealed to the watcher every detail of the bath's occupant.

Only a little steam disturbed the view. A perfect night for viewing, Captain T. . . . . . remarked to himself.

ARMED CUPID

A walk round the big city at this hour, when restraint is flushed from its coveys, tells everything about a nation's attitude to love. London is no more reserved in this than Manchester, Glasgow, Paris, Hamburg or Milan. Couples stand locked and lost in each other's fervour, kissing with ritualistic solemnity.

They are not bothered about where they are: it can be in the middle of the crowded concourse of Waterloo Station, forcing passengers wanting tea, coffee and chocolate from the vending machines to walk round them; or in a shaded doorway. These are the love drunks. They know not what they do.

Enslaved and entranced, they stand in the grimy passageway of *The Scene*. It is one of London's cellar clubs for the young; a blare of beat music, sub-aquatic lighting and coca-cola. Dancing couples are quietly lost in the ecstasy of solitary, mutual gyration. Where the lovers stand, somewhat away from the rest, the lighting is naked, unshaded. People pass all the while, bumping into them without heed or apology. They could move to a special "necking

132

alcove" with padded seats. They prefer the dirty, chilly awkwardness of the passage.

Ask them why, and they are immediately defensive. Is anything wrong with what they are doing? Why should they go in a pen with others? (There are plenty of others where they are.) Who cares?

Ask the management, and the defence is even more noticeable. They aren't doing anything improper. We keep an eye on them. They are only kids.

There are those who condemn Britain for making love so hard to come by. The Marriage Guidance Council's Rose Hacker, for one: "There is absolutely nowhere for young people to go and sit and talk," she says. "Youth clubs are still mainly in dreary old houses. Young lovers are often forced into immature relationships because their courtships are stunted. They marry long before they should, before they get to know each other fully, often with disastrous results."

Colonel Basil Brown of Butlins Holiday Camps is one who could do more for courting couples, but does not. "In Holiday Camps you don't provide an atmosphere of soft lights and sweet music," he explains. "I see to it there is no necking in any of our three types of dance-halls. If they want to do that sort of thing, they go for a walk on the beach. Young people create their own level. In things like that, they make their own way."

What of our behaviour police? The officials who regulate times of openings of parks, provision of clubs and centres, all the vast decor of social amenity which can nurture or knock out the fresh shoots of young love; what of them? At County Hall, there is a wise and humane man who has power over the national Cupid. His name is Mr Keeble; his job, supervising Youth Clubs. He says:

"My private view is that there are discoveries in this connexion, in this country, to be made. I think there must be a way found to accommodate and direct this form of feeling without it necesarily reaching serious courtship. Youth work is not a substitute for normal relationships of this sort, it is part of it. It can introduce young people to life and teach the beginnings of how to form a relationship. The social workers now tell me that there is less moral pressure abroad and I think this is healthy."

Another voice: that of Jean Medawar of Family Planning Association: "We're always being asked if we are being fair to young people in love, but being fair is not just a question of looking after their immediate needs, but of protecting them.

"Our society has removed chaperonage completely. The young now mature physically one year and ten months earlier than we did. Their parents give little or no impression of happiness in the later years of their marriage. What can you expect of them? They want to get all the fun they can as quickly as they can.

"Ask yourself, is it being fair to them to offer them a darkened bed in a darkened room, when they complain that they have nowhere to go to be together? It may be. But I have had a couple come to me to ask if they should sleep together—very much in love—and I took the weak way and said it was up to them. So they did, and the girl got into trouble. I still know her. I asked her recently, 'Would it have been better if I had dissuaded you?' She said 'oh, yes.' Well, there you are."

Before we leave the subject, Heather Jenner has a word to say. She is the warm, deeply understanding woman who runs Britain's best-known Marriage Bureau. I believe some 10,000 couples have been married as a result of her professional service. For Miss Jenner, British love problems break down into strict classes.

"The middle class have the hardest time at the moment," she says. "Working-class lovers 'go steady'; the upper class are getting a bit like that, too; but the 'mids'—hedged in by convention, locked in their suburbs—they are the ones who are finding it hard to 'get off'.

"Where do they go, poor things? Tennis clubs in the summer, mainly. And Young Conservative Clubs in the winter for a lot of them. But even there they are pretty well chaperoned, which makes it all very difficult.

"You see, chaperones are not really 'in' any more with the upper classes. Oh, debs still have somebody *with* them, but that's all mere ornament really. And of course the working classes just let them get on with it. But neither of these types has got the real 'respectability stuffing' which the mids have.

"Uppers and lowers don't mind what people say about them so much. Take a family like the Churchills. You can compare them quite easily to a bunch of lovers. If they happen to have some member of the family in disgrace—perhaps he or she goes off his head or goes to prison—they don't care. But the mids would. They're suburban. And conventional. And they get their only chances at the local singing group, the carol groups, the amateur dramatics and operatics.

"They can't hold hands in the front room any more, because mids don't keep such a temple. The 'lounge' is always full. One of their best launching pads is the Church.

"That's why so many parsons come to me. They're sick of doting spins in the parish and dying for a real woman."

Look round the big city and you will find evidence of these views on all sides.

WHAT IS LOVE?

"To talk and jest together, to do kind offices by turns, to read together honied books, to play the fool or be earnest together, to dissent at times without discontent as a man might do with his own self, and even with the solemness of these dissentings to season our more frequent consentings. Sometimes to teach and sometimes to learn, to long for the absent with impatience and to welcome the coming with joy."

St. Augustines's "Confessions"

It is the secret sympathy
The silver link, the silken tie,
Which heart to heart, and mind to mind
In body and in soul can bind.

Sir Walter Scott

As he turned into his drive, Clive L...... felt the enormous tiredness of the last twenty-four hours hit him like cramp. He should have phoned Angela from the office. Then she could have had something ready for him on a tray, and he could have had his bath and gone straight to bed. What had he forgotten to do for her? His mind, as always now when he thought about his home life, distilled a small, numb ache of dislike.

The garage doors were shut. Cursing, he had to get out in the light drizzle to open them. No lights were showing in the front of the house. Perhaps she was out? He almost looked in her garage alongside, but decided it was too much fag. He let himself in by the latch, surprised to find the lock secured in the open position so that his key would not turn. The hall was in darkness. Then he saw a thin strip of light under the living-room door ahead of him and heard voices.

There was a sudden shriek of laughter, high-pitched and excited. Not Angela. He did not recognize it and was curious. A man said something which he could not catch and the girl who was laughing spoke. She had a pronounced foreign accent. He recognised the *au-pair* girl who had not been with them long. She came from Ste-Maxime on the Côte, and had always seemed to him a rather mousey, uninteresting little thing with a permanently sniffling nose. What had brought her to life?

He walked across the hall and opened the door. They were

sitting in front of the fire, with the coffee table between them taking the cards. The first thing he noticed was Angela's bare back. It was towards him, and he could see the white strap marks left by her bathing costume. It occurred to him that she was sitting there with no clothes on.

They hadn't seen him come in and he had time to study the scene more carefully. Angela, he now saw, was dressed from the waist down, and was holding a loose brassiere across her breasts with one hand. Opposite her, in the armchair he thought of as his own, the *au-pair* girl was down to panties and bra, both black and frilled at the edges. Two men sat on the sofa, one of them vaguely recognizable as somebody from his wife's riding school. One had on only a singlet and underpants, the other was fully dressed except for his jacket.

"What the hell's going on?" asked Clive loudly from the doorway.

The group looked towards him unsteadily. They were drunk. Angela swung round in her chair and the covering over her front slipped. She made a considerable effort to restore dignity, then said solemnly in his direction: "Ah, Clive. How *nice* to see you. Nice trip? We're playing strip poker. Not quite your sort of game, is it?"

Clive felt anger boil inside him. "I think you'd all better get dressed and get out," he said. "You look disgusting."

The *au-pair* girl simpered. "Dees-gousting" she pronounced, leaning towards the man near her on the sofa. She overbalanced and fell on to his shoulder. It was the man with only singlet and drawers.

"What on earth got into you, Angela?" he asked. She had her back towards him again and was taking a long drink from a tall glass. "What the hell does this mean?"

"Wouldn't understand," she muttered vaguely, "wouldn't understand anything at all, would you Clive? Never mind. Never mind at all. You have your fun, I'll have mine, don't you think? Entitled, don't you see? Entitled."

He walked over, ignoring the others, facing her from behind the sofa. "Angela," he cried. "What's got into you? What's happened, for God's sake?"

She looked at him almost amiably, so that he knew how drunk she was.

"You wouldn't know, would you" she said. "You wouldn't know somebody called Vicky was here to tea with me. Of course not, darling. Not quite what you expected, was it?"

136

Good grief, he thought. So that was it.

"Angela," he said. "I'm going up to bed. Get these people out of here. I'll talk to you in the morning." He had to bite back the last words "when you're sober" which formed in his head. There was no point in antagonizing her.

"Well, he asked me upstairs to hear his records and when I got into his flat he pulled out a knife, held it to my throat and tried to tear my dress off. It was a lovely dress and I didn't want it torn, so . . ." she shrugged her pretty shoulders.

Christine Keeler, as reported by a newspaper

Between nine and midnight, that's when the divorces begin; when the infidelities and treacheries are discovered. In every year from 1958 to 1962 the divorce total rose. In 1958 it was 25,584. By 1962 it had become 33,818. A fact which ought to tie in somewhere is that there were more illegitimate births than divorces. In 1961, 49,107 babies were born out of wedlock. Nearly 50,000 a year in this country alone! So that a man's lifetime might see a population increase of three and a half million bastards.

And in Scotland, please note, the proud boast of having the lowest divorce rate in Europe, if not the Western world, was marred by another statistic: Scotland also had the highest suicide rate. Make what you like of that combination.

Love is a tyrant master. And at this hour it is showing its claws. A man in the Midlands, accused of fathering a woman's twins, is standing on a chair in the belfry of his local church, trying a belt of rope round his neck so that his body will be discovered half an hour before the double-wedding to be celebrated tomorrow.

In the Western United States, an English girl's body is being dismembered and stuffed into a trunk by her jealous lover, who first strangled her, then tortured her, then cut out her heart.

The hour is not for the timid. From now until midnight, Cupid goes armed.

Chapter 19

10 p.m.

OLD ADAM

If lovers' lanes and the back seats of parked motorcars are the altars of love's passion, an English pub is where the question more often than not gets popped; indecent proposals made. Over a smoky gin the words are much easier to find, in this last period before closing time and the all-enveloping arms of the night outside.

Queenie was used to such suggestions. After all it was her profession, in a semi-amateur but wholly dedicated sort of way. She had been on the game, on and off, since her father died five years ago. She was a strong, dark girl with large bones and well-moulded, fleshy face. Listening to the stranger with the carnation in his button-hole, and whisky on his breath, she screwed up her heavily made-up eyes against the smoke.

"You and me," he was saying, "why don't we take a bottle and find somewhere to celebrate. It's not every day I bring home an accumulator."

"You're joking."

"I'll tell you what I'll do. What's your name?"

138

"Queenie."

"Ay, well, Queenie; I'll tell you what I'll do. I'll take a room at the best bloody hotel in the place, if you'll come with me. The best bloody hotel."

"Don't be daft. The Grand? I wouldn't be seen dead in the dump."

"Well, anywhere then."

She looked at him as she always did at the men in her life. Chance they might be, but she didn't take all comers. A girl could be choosey. It wasn't as if the game was all she had to depend on.

He was a rat-like man in a sharply creased green tweed suit, but his eyes were young and steady. She liked the sardonic set of his mouth; the way he had of tapping his cigarette gently against the ashtray as he talked.

It didn't take much to make up her mind, and he had just enough she decided.

"All right, *Nubar*," she said, finishing her gin at a swig. "I'll celebrate with you. Get a little bottle of gin then, for me. But there's no sense in spending a lot of money on a room when mine's going begging, is there?"

He smiled broadly. "Marvellous," he said. "Bloody marvellous. You're a wonderful girl and I'm just faintly partial to you, even without the bloody drink, I'll have you know."

"Aye. Well, enough of the bullshit."

"No. Honest." His eyes were wide and innocent and she had to smile.

"We'll see," she said. He turned to the bar as the landlord came over to shout time and ordered a half of Gordons and one of Haig.

"How far away's your place?" he asked. "Do we need a taxi?"

"We might as well."

In the old Daimler, smelling of horsehair and vomit, she lay back in the corner and let him kiss her. He was hungry for a woman, she thought. Her experienced mind reckoned the possibilities, deciding he would most likely be hard to get rid of. She had her sister's child coming in the morning, all the way from Shrewsbury by train. She'd promised to meet her.

"Go easy, Casanova," she whispered. "I thought we were going to celebrate."

His reply was a physical definition of man's single-mindedness.

At the entrance to her flat she had a job disengaging. He was strong and half-way drunk and his fingers were like pincers. She

139

had to kick him on the shin with the sharp side of her shoe before he would come to his senses and let her get out. The taxi-driver was embarrassed. He managed only a gruff "thanks" for the proffered pound note.

To the clank of the bottles in his pockets, they climbed the stairs to the second floor. The shaded orange light was on in her hallway, as she always left it when she went out; never knowing how or with whom she might return. She took off her coat and skipped out of his reach into the kitchenette for glasses. She found a bottle of tonic water in a cupboard, and an opener.

He was lighting a cigarette with concentrated effort when she rejoined him in the bed-sitting room. She turned the switch on the record player and lifted the pick-up arm on the record resting on the turntable. The music was throbbing, beaty.

He had wrenched the foil off the bottle of Gordons gin and was pouring her a drink. "Leave some room for the tonic," she said.

He grunted. "Here. And forget about the bloody world," he said. He picked up his own glass, already half-filled with neat Scotch. "You're a bloody good girl," he said. "Bloody good."

They drank, then he assumed a curiously old-fashioned pose and pantomimed an invitation to dance with him. She let him take her, knowing the outcome and wondering how she was going to switch off the record so that the needle wouldn't get even more worn down than it was already.

He was like a frightened, ravenous animal when they got to it. She tried to help him, but he was blinded by passion and greed for her body.

Anybody's body, she told herself with a taste of bitterness. Five years had taught her something about men's carnal desires.

From her point of view, it could have been satisfactory. He was a light-weight eleven stone or thereabouts, and the gin had anaesthetized her against too much sensitivity. She wasn't bothered by his rapacity, until he began to flag.

She sensed it almost before he did, and tightened her legs.

They both tried then. It was no use. After a lot of grunting, sweating effort he began to curse. She suddenly tired and wrenched him away from her. "Let's have a drink," she said.

He lay still for a moment, breathing heavily. Then he rolled off the divan and picked himself up. He came over to the bed with his glass in his hand.

"You're a big cow, but you're not much bloody good to a man, are you?" he said nastily.

She felt angry and insulted. "Who's a man, then?" she asked shrilly.

He looked down at her, swaying. Then he put down the glass of whisky on the bedside table and picked up the bottle. She saw it in the air above his head before he brought it down on her skull, knocking the sense out of her.

Prostitutes in this country are regarded with less tolerance than homosexuals. According to "Television and Religion," a poll report prepared on behalf of A.B.C. Television and published by University of London Press, six out of every ten people condemned prostitutes while only three out of every ten, or rather less, felt that homosexuals should be punished by law. Even with another 27 per cent, who thought the men should be condemned but not punished, the women were still less popular.

You poor thing. Don't you see that the only reason Englishmen have affairs is a pitiful attempt to prove you are men. But it is meaningless. You indulge in furtive seductions. Yet you never make a woman feel you are a real he-man. It is all so unreal.

It is not true masculinity, the kind that makes a woman curl up with submission to a man. You have no male presence. Only a boudoir manner.

The things you talk about. No American man knows anything about decorating a room. We each have our spheres in America. Husbands have their jobs. Women run the home. But you have it all mixed up. In a matriarchy at least you can tell the sexes apart.

Look, I am really only saying that, for all your talk about sex, you have forgotten how to keep men and women apart. You don't pamper women with courtesies or exalt men as heads of the house. You aren't masculine or feminine. You are hermaphrodites.

An anonymous American, reported by columnist
Quentin Crew

All peoples of the world have realised that whilst small quantities of alcohol excite the amorous appetite and remove annoying inhibitions, excessive quantities produce a temporary impotence, an inability to effect the act, despite a possible strong desire.

Translated from the "Kuttanimatam" by Powys Mathers

"Are you sure you wouldn't rather have a gin?" Mr C......
was smiling. He had a dusty bottle of brown ale in his hand and an opener. Arthur shook his head. "No thanks," he said.

Mr C...... opened the bottle, holding it away from him and carefully wiping the rim with a clean handkerchief, where the cap had covered it, before pouring out. He handed the glass and the bottle, still a quarter full, to Arthur. "There you are," he said, "honest ale for an honest young man. How old are you, Arthur?"

"Sixteen. Well, nearly seventeen. In March, I will be."

"A good age; a beginning, really. Here's hoping you'll find what you most enjoy."

They raised their glasses, Mr C......'s cut-glass tumbler with the iridescent facets and colourless contents against Arthur's negroid cone. "Cheers."

They drank in silence. When Arthur looked again in Mr C......'s direction the tumbler was empty. Mr C......'s eyes were softer and moister than before. He had put the empty glass on the book-case, beside the heavy cut-glass decanter. "Look Arthur," he said, "I've got to go out later on." He felt his chin as though testing the protrusion of his beard. "Would you mind if I had a shave?"

"No. I'm all right. Better be going soon as I've finished this," he held up his glass. "I'm not s'fast as you, am I?"

Mr C...... laughed rather loudly. "You're doing fine," he said, "and there's not the least reason for you to hurry. Going somewhere?"

"No. I'll have to get home some time, that's all."

"What were your plans when we ... I mean, outside the gun-shop. If I hadn't invited you back here, what would you have done with your evening?"

"Probably gone to the flicks, I s'pose. Or to the Bowling."

"Alone?"

"Might have seen some of m'mates there."

"What about girls? Surely a big handsome fellow like you has plenty of adorable girl friends."

"I'm through with birds."

Mr C...... laughed again. "So am I, to tell you the truth Arthur," he said. His voice was warm and familiar. "Deceitful creatures. Treacherous too."

"You can ruddy say that again." The beer was warming Arthur's inside, making him feel more confident than he had since he had arrived inside this posh flat. "Yes, you can ruddy say that again," he repeated.

"You know, Arthur," Mr C...... had poured himself another neat gin. His voice had sobered. He was like an affectionate schoolmaster. "A man of the world has no need for the sort of women who ply their wiles on you, their disgusting little wiles, and expect you to sit up begging for more. Don't you agree?"

Arthur wiped his mouth with the back of his hand and tried to look as though he understood. "I dunno," he mumbled. "I s'pose so." Then a thought struck him.

"'ere," he said suddenly, "what's your name? You 'aven't told me yet."

Mr C. . . . . . smiled to cover the process of selection that was going on in his head. "That's right," he said finally. "I'm Masters. Colin Masters."

"What do you work at? I mean, what sort of job do you do then, Mr Masters?"

"Call me Colin if you like. I don't."

"You mean you don't do no work? What do you do all day then?"

"Oh, I have . . . interests."

"Cor! I reckon I would 'n all if I didn't have a bleedin' job to keep me out of mischief all day long."

"You think you'd get into mischief, do you Arthur?"

"You're bloody right, mate. Cor!"

"But I thought you said you'd gone off girls?"

"Yeh. Well. They're no good are they? Like you just said, they're a thievin', lyin', cheatin' bunch of whores, that's what they are."

"So what sort of mischief would you get up to, eh Arthur?" Mr C. . . . . . was leaning forward, over the arm of Arthur's chair. He spoke softly, almost meekly. Then he laughed.

"I'd better go and get that shave, if I'm going to," he said.

After he had gone, Arthur wasn't altogether sure why he felt a relaxation of inner tension; but he did. How much so he realized when, a few moments later, his host reappeared.

Mr C. . . . . . was wearing a heavy, flowered-silk dressing gown and, to judge from his smooth, bare calves, had removed his trousers. Above the circle of chest exposed by the neck hole of his blue silk singlet a mass of foamy lather encircled his chin.

He had a book in one hand with a picture on the cover of a well-built, naked, young man seen from behind. His weight was on one leg, the other trailing. And his hands were linked and drawn down below his buttocks. "Have a look at these, Arthur," said Mr C. . . . . . . "They might amuse you."

To emphasize the personal and private nature of moral or immoral conduct is to emphasize the personal and private responsibility of the individual for his own actions, and that is a responsibility which a mature agent can properly be expected to carry for himself without the threat of punishment from the law. We accordingly recommend that homosexual behaviour between consenting adults in private should no longer be a criminal offence.

Report of the Committee on Homosexual Offences and Prostitution
(HMSO '57)

... No criminal code is or can be the same as a moral code, whether regarded as divinely inspired or nor ... the criminal law is not a statement of how people ought to behave; it is a statement of what will happen to them if they do not behave.

"The Enforcement of Morals", Sir Patrick Devlin.
(Given as Maccabaean Lecture in Jurisprudence to
the British Academy, 1959)

Chapter 20

11 p.m.

EROTIC MOULD

"Goldie, Tim wants you!" The shout, from the doorway of the Press Club bar, turned Peter S...... He nodded and doubled across the room. "Your change, Mr S......?" one of the white-jacketed barmen called after him. "Keep it for me."

He was down the lino-ed stairs two at a time, out through the swing doors into Salisbury Court. The rain had become a light drizzle. Two minutes, and he was sliding his bulk along the chairs of the back bench towards the slight, dark man in the centre. "You wanted me, sir?"

"Yes, Goldie. What do you know about *Mamaxin?*"

"Sounds like a drug. One of the new ones?"

"It's more than that. Apparently, it's been given, orally, to women for years. To stop them getting pregnant. Now they've suddenly found it can deform the kids in some way. Like *Thalidomide,* but *after* the mums have stopped taking it. We had a reporter for the Diary covering the Royal Society dinner. It seems the whole thing came out in one of the speeches. Good story?"

Peter's dark, cautious eyes widened appreciatively. "Well, if it's not too late to talk.to some of the mums . . ." he said.

"Leave it to you. Watch your edition times."

Somebody was using his machine. He slung his jacket over a vacant chair-back and picked up one of the clutch of phones which, like plastic crabs, huddled in the centre of the two joined desks. A few moments later a smiling, gesticulating, conciliatory, bouncy, sober, deeply sympathetic (but too tough to show it) above all urgent and inquisitive Peter S . . . . . ., special writer, was hard at work.

Ironically, the tragedy being born in this lunar-lit office, against the maelstrom racket of typewriters and talk, was his own. His wife had taken the drug, on doctor's orders, to give her a rest between having their second child—a boy born only eleven months after his elder sister—and her third, now on its way.

But Peter did not know.

"Are you at all worried by the possibility, though, Mrs O . . . . . .?" he was saying. The ballpoint in his hand moved faster over the folded sheets of copy paper. "I see . . . you don't trust the medical profession. Your children have always been fine, healthy . . . how many have you, Mrs O . . . . . .?"

Forty minutes later, the story was on the editor's desk. Copies of it were being read simultaneously by the news editor, the lawyer and the chief sub editor. "Nice work, Goldie. That Lady Lewisham quote was a good idea. What made you think of her?"

"She likes pills, doesn't she? Lives on vitamins."

"Oh, aye. Well, that's it. With your piece on page one and the doctor's stuff splashed across the leader page . . ." the editor turned to the man beside him. "Get on to Dr C . . . . . ., Jack, and ask him to put a spurt on. We haven't got a page until he comes through, just a bloody great hole."

The editor and the reporter, enjoying a fine convalescent weariness now, looked at each other and smiled.

"Don't go too far, Goldie," said the editor quietly. "I have a feeling we haven't seen the back of this one for tonight."

They lay in the wet grass, three of them, watching the lane he would come down. At one moment the clouds parted and moonlight shone on the thin steel trip-wire stretched across the road. It soon vanished.

By a quarter past, the smallest, best-dressed of the three

146

looked at his watch by quickly igniting a cigarette-lighter. "He'll be along directly," he said. At that moment they heard the crack of twigs and the rustling sound of a bicycle wheels on mould.

Henry M...... was used to cycling along these lanes in the dark. His lighting equipment was hardly strong enough to show him where the bends lay, but this gave him no concern. He'd been born and brought up in Mycklem. Weren't many places he didn't know hereabouts.

Knew his way to Mrs S......'s bungalow right enough, no doubt about that. He chuckled as he thought about it. That was up near where the old bungalow kept by that queer bee-keeping gentleman had stood, before it'd burnt down. She and her husband had picked a nice spot to live; if it was woodland you favoured.

He didn't fancy it much himself. Too many creepy-crawlies. Still, it was nice inside the caravan, no mistake about it. First time she'd invited him in he'd gone more from curiosity than anything else. Never been inside of one of them before.

The bedroom stuck in his mind most. It was the living-room too, in a way. But it had a curtained sort of recess at one end where the double-bed lay, and to his mind this shed an air of intimacy over the whole place.

That was where they slept at night; made love, too. He thought about that. But later on, after he knew her better, he realized that it hadn't been that way a long time, not with them.

Mr S...... wasn't kind to her, at least that was what she said. He looked a hard man. He had an ugly set to his jaw and his eyes weren't friendly either. Lucky for Henry he had to travel about the country so much on business, in his firm's car.

Must have been the first time after he'd met them, after he'd gone up to saw the logs for her, that she'd offered him a cup of tea inside the caravan. He hadn't needed second bidding. She looked, as he thought, "proper eatable" in her pale pink nylon housecoat. He washed his hands under the pump, flecked some water over his dark, strong, curly hair and went to the doorway.

"I wonder if you'd mind taking your boots off?" she asked him. The invitation seemed deliciously cosy. It made him feel like a cold animal given warmth and kindness.

Later, she let him kiss her and undress her without any fuss. She seemed to know what he was going to do from the moment he started. As they made love she moaned frantically, like a child in the grip of a nightmare. His native sense told him she was repressed.

147

They didn't talk about themselves for some time after that. He came whenever she asked, sending him notes to his cottage and, if he was out, leaving them with his old mother, who always knew where to find him. His hours made it easy for them both, because his farm duties up at Captain C......'s left him free the best part of the day. They never spent a whole night together.

While her husband was away on his trips, Henry would come to the caravan after his tea and leave about ten or eleven, anyway before midnight. His bike was an asset, it meant he could be home in not much over fifteen minutes.

There had been times, recently, when he hadn't been so keen to go up to see Mrs S...... It was all very well; a man tired of doing nothing but going with a woman all the spare time he had. He wanted to go down to the pub and play a bit of darts, like he'd been used to doing before he met her. Sly remarks from some of his cronies didn't upset his easy-going nature, but they rankled.

She became emotional when he missed an evening. For about three minutes, while he stood on the step the next night, she refused to answer the door. When she did come her face was white and her eyes blazing. She was like a cat, spitting with suppressed fury and hurt. He had no words to pretend or to lie to her. He just said his bike had had a puncture, which it had, and left it at that. She soon wept and made it up. That time.

There were other times, and she was not always so easily consoled. At times she railed and ranted at him. He barely understood what she was on about. Finally, she went to her handbag and took out two crumpled pound notes. "Here," she said, thrusting them into his hands. "Take this and *make sure* you come tomorrow. Please."

He'd taken the money because that was his way. If people offered, it was impolite to refuse, he'd been taught. Going home that night he felt like throwing the whole thing over. He was sick of it. But he was there the following evening, on time.

She'd taken to giving him money since then. Every time, before he left, she'd slip him one or two pound notes. He began to wonder what to do with it all. It was his normal practice to keep all his savings in the big bible over his mother's bed, but the notes were beginning to swell out the old book and threaten its binding.

This night he'd been unavoidably late, having been called out to free a terrier caught in a gamekeeper's squirrel trap. The poor little dog, not much more than a puppy, was in danger of losing several inches of one fore-leg. Henry had bathed and set the broken limb, tying a rough splint to hold the fractured bone until the vet came. The little dog had lain its head against his jacket and whimpered piteously. At that moment he felt more sympathy for this one animal than for the whole human race with its wiles and traps and villainies.

She hadn't taken kindly to his terse explanations. "Oh, so that's it," she'd said. "Anything comes before me, of course, I should know that by now."

He felt a surge of anger. "The dying come before the dead," he said. It was a phrase he had picked up somewhere, probably from one of the cheap novels he sometimes read solemnly to himself before going to sleep. It had some vague connexion with stretcher bearers and a battle-front, but he couldn't place it. Why he had used it now he could not really say.

"Oh, so I'm an old corpse am I?" she screamed at him. "Well, I'd like to know what that makes *you*. I'd just like to know that."

It was sometimes better when they fought. He found it easier to take her afterwards. And the knowledge in the back of his brain that he'd soon be on his bike and away, with two of her pound notes in his pocket, was sufficient incentive. Tonight was no different from others.

But the men waiting in the dark lane knew differently. They were not from the village, not from this part of the country. The short one had a strong Liverpool accent; almost a brogue. His two accomplices were thick-set, grey-faced men. One wore a shapeless city overcoat of what had once been navy blue melton and the other was in a heavy, dirty, quilted zipper-jacket.

Mr S...... had brought them here and shown them the path and the point where the two birches stood on either side so that they could tie the trip wire across. He had even supplied them with the wire, before leaving in his motorcar. He had a long drive ahead of him, back to Wolverhampton and the cinema he was supposed to be spending his evening in.

Half the money went with him. He'd shown the whole amount to the trio's leader, given him exactly half and arranged where the other half could be collected after the job had been done satisfactorily. It came to £400 all together: £200 now and £200 later.

They lay still. Henry's bike was coming towards them, so close now that its sickly yellowing light flashed on the tree trunks and shrubs concealing them. They could even hear his heavy breathing like a subdued grunt, as he trod his weight on the pedals, forcing the tyres over the slow surface of the lane.

Then he was on it, and there was a sudden, taut "plunk" as

the wire sprang. The bike collapsed and caterpaulted him forward. He landed heavily on his right shoulder. They were on to him before he could raise his head to see their faces.

Three men with knives and coshes. A brutal job, even messier than the trap which had fractured the terrier's fore-leg. But effective. Henry M......was too stunned to recover consciousness before he bled to death. In the event, the light from his battery lamp lasted longer than he did.

It is a matter of forensic interest only that Henry M......'s murder—a sort of British *crime passionelle*—occurred at precisely the same moment, as far as can be ascertained, when Arthur brought the cut-glass whisky decanter down on Mr C......'s head for a reason which sexual reformers in Britain might find interesting. Arthur was neither adult nor consenting, and Mr C...... was trying to kiss him.

Chapter 21

Midnight

WITCHING HOUR

From inside a passing motorcar the grey houses seem wrapped in
sleep and silence. Very little stirs in the cities, nothing at all in
the country. There is an air of private but at the same time shared
respectability; a feeling that nothing savage or barbaric can possibly happen; that Peter O'Toole, the actor, is out of cerebral
control when he says—as wont to do—that "there are more
petty tyrannies behind the potted palms of Clapham than you'll
find in all the Hampstead and Chelsea homes of the acting profession." Yet the truth is in the *News of the World* each Sunday.
If it is not pretty, then at least it supports those who believe in
British vitality and initiative.

Big Ben, hammering out its sonorous dozen, stands above a
rash of different-sized, different talking and widely different-
tempered Britons, less of whom are actually tucked up and asleep
at this hour than the habit-measuring statisticians would imagine.
To cast a quick eye over our own tiny motley: Dr. de S...... is
casting no shadow; nevertheless, he is up to something nefarious.

Not with Inge, his intellectual mistress in Hampstead. Her

151

phone did not answer, so he has taken a taxi from Caxton Hall, where the meeting was, to his club in St James's Square, and there put through a discreet telephone call.

The bed he is now sitting on, somewhat ruefully in his shirt tails, is faintly warm from the not-so-long-departed body of Detective-Sergeant Hubert L....... The woman adjusting her suspender belt by the wardrobe is the tart we made acquaintance with earlier. Now that her ponce is in jail, remanded to appear on the distasteful charge of "living on immoral earnings", she is working for two. She'll be tired in the morning, she knows. But she couldn't very well refuse the doctor. After all, she's known him for such a long time. And he, at least, has never been any trouble; not like some of them. He just prefers her not to get fully undressed, that's all. Because, he says, it reminds him of his wife.

Vivienne de S......, mentally and physically exhausted—yet transported—by her latest and most convincing encounter with the spirit world, and with her floppy-haired, remembered school-boy-hero, Jim (who has thrillingly asked her if she "still finds her homework hard to do") is sipping lemon-tea with the other ladies and wondering why the handsome dark-eyed medium from Cardiff, Mme Eloise A......, is still trying to hold her hand, at times even pressing her leg above the knee under the small coffee-table, now that the séance is over.

What has become of the others? Of Fred F......, facing his personal Armageddon at the hands of a sympathetic, quasi-envious law? He sits in his 'dingly-dell', as the lags used to call their box-like homes, and tries not to think the same thoughts over and over again. He is supposed to be in bed. But the discomfort, the strangeness and the worry, like bile in his mind, prevent this. There is no fun or future in being Fred F...... at this moment, though his sin is not enormous and he has physically harmed nobody. The fact is he has stepped out of line, disclosing his sexual propensity. In a civilized country, that will never do. Invoking the shades of Kraft-Ebbing and Havelock Ellis will not do either. Fred must take his punishment.

Clive L......, on the other hand . . . isn't he more sinned against than sinning? The moralists might think so. He is a cheap and lecherous adulterer (one can hear the Old Bailey judge clicking his tongue over such a phrase) but surely a man has a right to find his wife upholding the moral line? Strip poker in one's own sitting-room, and with one's own *au-pair* girl! Hell, what next?

So Clive thinks, anyway, as he lies alone in the right-hand of the twin divan beds listening to the sounds of final departure below and, at welcome last, the slam of the front door and a car's engine outside. Only when he has fully tested the silence does he realize that his wife and the au pair girl have both left him. He is surprised at the feeling of loneliness which the knowledge brings with it.

And Margie B......? She is in the bicycle shed at the back of Ron's father's cottage. He has his arms round her, their bodies rest against one another; but they are talking seriously and have been doing so now for nearly two hours. Both are cold and tired. However hard they try to find a solution, none seems available. Margie sighs, knowing there *is* none; only the baby and the ordeal she must bear.

Our two beat-chicks—remember them?—are at a folk-do. A thin man with heavily scarred face, and a beard simulating a latter-day Don Quixote, is playing his guitar and singing old, passionate ballads which roll in the head like thunder or the sound of battle. They sit on the floor, her bandaged head against one of his drawn up-knees. There is a smell of resinous sweat and flour-hacks. Candles gutter in wine bottles, mostly Algerian, as the rising wind forces entry under the barn door. He finds her flesh under the top of her jeans where her spinal column makes a canal at the back, and squeezes gently. The singer describes the sad, cruel drowning of an unrequited country lover. She turns to smile up at him with pin-pointed pupils. "Later," she promises.

This is busy-busy time at the high-class call-girl pad backing onto Etna Street, W.1. Two of the girls, blonde Clarice and Cynthia, are packing to drive into the country for the rest of the night; a chauffeur-driven Rolls-Bentley is even now waiting outside. Their services have been specially requested, by a marquess whose wife is in an alcoholics' sanatorium in the Bahamas. The hand-written note which the chauffeur brought with him has expressly asked them to wear riding-habit.

Ma'am is busy, in what the girls laughingly, but accurately, call the "torture chamber". She has two customers, one paying her £30, the other £50, whose clothes she has taken away before chaining them up in this dark, chilly room, with only the one naked electric light bulb high up near the ceiling, and the uncurtained window wide open. She has then flogged them with a cat-o'-nine-tails.

Ma'am neither knows nor cares (since the Police are such friends of hers) that Pip, Duke of S......, is giving a small party next door, in his town flat; or that her neighbour has been aware for some time of the nature of the establishment that borders his own. At his suggestion, the guests are gleefully listening to the proceedings in the "torture chamber"—placing tumblers to the intervening wall so as to increase the volume of the sound. Among them is a member of the Royal Family, who seems to be enjoying the *divertissement* as much as anyone present.

Earlier the Duke has regaled his guests with excerpts from the private diary he earlier stole from his wife's boudoir. He has spent some time, for their entertainment, hilariously comparing it with his own. It has been remarked that on nights when the Duchess waxed, the Duke waned; and vice versa. The whole subject has led to a high state of intelligent interest and erotic excitement; though the latter will not become evident until later on.

In the lowland Scottish police court where the body of eighteen year old Evelyn H...... has been taken, great activity seethes. The Yard has been called in. An eminent pathologist is now examining the body, deducing from the bruises on her arms and the small knife pricks in her back that she was forced to the place where she died, then stabbed to death during sexual intercourse. It seems that her perverted killer gained full sexual satisfaction at the point when he repeatedly stabbed her through the heart. There is only one suspect at present: the milkman who found her. He claims not to have touched the body, but tests suggest otherwise.

Who else? Maureen J...... and her lover Tim are celebrating as planned, but they have been lured into accepting a casual invitation to a boring party in a Camden Hill bed-sitting room. The gin has run out, the room is full of smoke and two men are threatening to punch each other's heads. Maureen, on the floor by the record player which is deafening her, says quite soberly to an almost asleep Timothy. "I'm tired, darling. Shall we be gone?"

Outside a plane drones across the sky. Mrs. Bonny R...... flanked by two well-built women military police sergeants, occupies one of the few passenger seats in the converted trooper. Her husband's body, in a sealed, travelling coffin, lies behind her, in the plane's tail. Mrs R......'s mind is numb. All she can think of is Bridie's face when they led her away.

But if these are astir, Sam S...... is only restless. At home, in suburban Farley Road, he is enjoying one of his rare nights when sleep has not been deliberately interrupted by his jealous wife, Edith. The hot-water bottle is not leaking. There is no trace of itching powder, rusty barbed-wire, or stinging nettles, in his bed.

Still he can't sleep. He lies awake wondering what he'll do, now that she has left him and gone back to her mother. Wishing she were here, tormenting him.

Above the masseur's, two others are composed for sleep yet still awake. Mr Max L......, the proprietor, has things on his mind. Miranda, his companion, is shy. They will be tired in the morning.

Oh yes, and Candida R......'s headmistress is awake, staring into the darkness of her bedroom, wondering about Candida's private life and liaisons. Wondering too how it was that she, at the same age, blushed furiously every time an eligible young man spoke to her, and rarely found time for anything more social than a concert with her parents or a family party.

Candida, at least, is asleep, alone, and dreaming sweet dreams.

A woman and her fifteen-year-old daughter made persistent midnight visits to a man's home, though he had told them to keep away, a court was told.

But the couple—partly in their nightclothes—forced him to let them in by knocking loudly on the door and disturbing his neighbours.

Then . . . the girl would sleep with him while her mother lay on top of the bed.

Report in the NEWS OF THE WORLD

It was nearly half past twelve as the coven assembled on the low, cushioned seats against the walls of Brian C......'s Leeds flat. The only lights came from the thick black candles flaming in the wall sconces. In their glow, Angeline looked deathly pale.

She was wearing a diaphanous white gown of sheer nylon under which her otherwise unclad figure was clearly visible. Her limbs trembled slightly though the room, heated by large radiators, was warm.

At first there was only a subdued hum of talk from the other witches gathering in the wall-seats. As their number increased, however, the noise grew in volume. Brian's entry was unnoticed for a second or two, so intent were they on their conversation.

He was wearing black satin boxing trunks and a black cape which at some time might have dignified the shoulders of a schoolmaster. His iron grey hair, freshly washed and combed, glistened pale silver in the candle-light. On it, he wore a golden crown. In any circumstances he was an astonishing sight; but in the bizarre setting of the room his presence seemed laughably melodramatic.

Now he approached the altar circle with firm, almost jaunty, steps. He turned. Raising one hand, he commanded an immediate hush. "Good evening," he said. "I'm sorry to have kept you waiting, but this as you know is rather a special occasion for the coven. Angeline and I are to be married."

A low hum of approval purred out of the seated audience. Among them were rather more men than women, their average age perhaps only a shade under thirty-five. Brian turned to a tall slim man who had followed him to the altar. "Donald is now going to perform the ceremony for us," he said. "I hope you can remember it all, Don?"

The tall thin man inclined his head in assent. He did not smile. Against the cabalistic signs painted on the obelisk-type cupboard behind him, it was easy to imagine Donald with small horns sticking out of his hair.

"All right then," said Brian briskly. "Let's get on with it."

He moved across to Angeline and took her arm, leading her, none too gently, down the centre of the room towards the circular black space in the middle of the floor where the altar was drawn. At the edge of the circle, marked with David's star and other symbols, they knelt. The black service began.

Half an hour later the couple had been joined in unholy matrimony; as "man and his woman, under the terms and ancient rites of 'the craft', and unbreakable except by its own laws and invocations." She wore a heavy gold ring which he had put on her right hand. Together, they had leapt, barefoot, through flames from a burning cauldron.

While silken cord fastened their arms together, Donald gingerly sliced their wrists with a razor blade until a speck of blood showed on each. This was smeared together by the couple.

It completed the ceremony. By then, Angeline's colour had returned to her cheeks. She stood listening to the black mass, intoned by the people round her, her young breasts rising and falling with excitement.

And, later, as the orgy began, she threw herself into her "husband's" arms, surrendering herself to the full consequences of her action.

Outside, a man is speaking into the mouthpiece of a public telephone. He is scruffy and unshaven. His breath smells of stale rum. The cigarette stub in the corner of his mouth is blackened and cold. He talks slowly, rubbing his pink-rimmed eyes with a dirty handkerchief and swaying uncomfortably on his broken shoes.

"I've got a story for you," he croaks. "Witches. If you'll pay me I can tell you it all. All about witchcraft in this country, what they get up to, everything. You'll have to pay me well, but it's a true story."

At the other end, a tired voice crackles something to the effect that "this newspaper doesn't buy stories on spec. just because somebody rings up out of the bloody blue at 12.40 in the morning! What's it all about?" Anyone familiar with its tones would recognize Goldie's voice. He is still in the office.

"You don't understand, young feller," says the man. "I'm an ordained high priest of Satan! That's what I am. I've put on dozens of ceremonies—Solstices included. Do you know what they do at Solstices twice a year—yes, even in this country? Do you?"

"What do they do?"

"They sacrifice a living animal—a cat. They crucify it. I can tell you all about it, everything there is to know. About the virginal sacrifice, too. You know about *that*, don't you?"

"No and I'm not sure I want to, thank you. Look old man," Goldie is beginning to feel sickened and bored at the same time. Also, he wants his supper. "I don't honestly think . . ."

The man cuts him off. "When they want to call a meeting of witches in this country," he says, "they put an advertisement in *The* bloody *Times* Personal Column! I'm telling you! It reads like a dance, or something; but there's always one secret word in it, known only to all witches and followers of the craft. That's how they know. Then they see the time and place, because these apply to the next gathering."

Despite himself, Goldie is being drawn. "What sort of people go to these gatherings?" he asks.

"People like you and me, son. Bloody great rich Americans with big cars. All sorts, you'd be astonished." He chuckles.

"I'll bet there's nothing much to them, really," says Goldie helplessly. The only chance now is to hang up; but he doesn't dare, for fear he'll miss something. "Anyway," he adds lamely. "How do I know you're telling the truth?"

The man chuckles again, with greater feeling. "You don't," he says. "I'll tell you frankly, matey, I'm in this racket for what I can get out of it. I'm a criminal, and ninety-nine out of every hundred who're in it are the same. What do you think?"

"You mean it's all cooked up to take money off the visitors?"

"That's it. We're supposed to have a nude virgin on the altar. A-a-a-a-g, she's no virgin! She's a bloody whore. We pay her to

157

come and do the show for us. And the bits of consecrated stuff we're supposed to have pinched from a holy place, like tombs and churches and the like, they're fake too. What we make most of our money out of, though, is the photos."

"What photos?"

"Well, we take pictures with infra-red light, so the flash won't show. During the orgies, you see. And then we've got 'em, haven't we? It's the best source of revenue, that is."

"I see." Goldie pauses, suddenly deeply disgusted with the whole conversation. "Well, thank you, but we won't be interested." He puts down the receiver, quickly. *Good God*, he thinks on his way back to the Press Club, *is it really possible?*

Chapter 22

1 a.m.

TOGETHERNESS

Englishmen retire early because they earnestly believe that eight hours' sleep a night does them good. A great many foreign visitors in consequence, tend to think they are sluggards. Nothing could be farther from the truth, as we all know.

This is the curious half-world between wakefulness and full retirement, the time when English men and women are *in private* together. It is all-important to notice the difference.

In public, they may behave as though physical contact between the sexes is something both distasteful and faintly obscene. At this hour of the night, they allow their great, passionate hearts to beat as one, their deeply romantic souls to entwine in embraces such as Cleopatra would have swooned over.

This is the time when an English lover sails on a sure course toward the heart and happiness of his beloved; when his soulmate gives him in return all the abandoned artistry of womanhood. Seeing them next day—him on the 8.23 and her at the supermarket —who would guess? Perhaps it is as well.

Not all are so well-intentioned, or well-behaved, as the millions

159

who live normal and satisfying married lives. There are always the odd men, and women, out.

Mrs B......, for instance, is not soul-satisfied or impassioned. She is begrudging the hour so much as the occasion. "How *could* you, Margie?" she asks over and over again, literally wringing her work-worn hands in front of the tired girl. Poor Margie. It has been a hell of a day; one she will remember as long as she lives. She has not been home since Dr F...... dropped her at her gate. She ran, then, all the way round to Ron's place. And luckily he was in, doing some very complicated homework.

It was Ron's advice which made her tell her mother; made her promise on Guides' honour that she would. What else—apart from the suicide she toyed with almost hourly—could she *possibly* do? The doctors had both been immensely kind. They had gone to no end of trouble over her—as though she had contracted some dreadful form of madness, she thought, which might infect others. Nobody had suggested a single plausible way in which she might escape her impossible dilemma. Her mother was her last chance, one she reached only when her more acute sensitivities had been washed out and blunted by over-exposure; by exhaustion, too; and by cold, creeping misery. Margie was so unhappy it was like a great, numbing weight on her soul.

She knew what to expect from her mother, of course. Margie was an only child; her mother's heroine, her one proof of conquest over a churlish and grudging world. The few words she used to impart the terrible information: "Mum, I'm going to have a baby," could never have demolished a human being more completely. Mrs B...... looked across at her daughter through an agonized, unbelieving haze until at last she became sure she was telling the truth, however out of all question it seemed; and then the dams of despair broke within her.

It was not the sin of it that distressed her. No woman, in such a crisis, concerns herself with moral attitudes. She was a mother, wounded by her own, that was the nature of the agony inside her. The dagger in her breast had, so to speak, her daughter's hand still on its haft. This was a time for self-criticism as much as rebuke.

Margie could tell her almost nothing. *How* it had happened; *why?*; *what* she had been thinking of . . . all these were abstracts, several millenia from the centre of her misery. She saw her mother's reasons for seeking answers to such questions, but was incapable of giving even the solace of these. All Margie could say was that it had happened; that she hadn't meant it to; that she was sorry, and frightened, and desperately upset; and please, please don't make her go back to school.

"What'll I do with you, then?" Mrs . . . . . .'s voice was harsh with anxiety.

"Hide me! Go away! Anything, mum; only don't make me go back. I can't! I won't!"

"How long has it been, then? Since you went with him?"

"Four months."

The mother was silent, thinking. She was weighing a possibility. Robert had been a good friend, and persistent in asking her to marry him this past twelve-month. Could she bear another man, another master, to clothe and feed and slave for; after all she'd known? She squared her thin shoulders.

"Well, there might be a way," she said. "You'll have to help me, mind."

"What are you going to do?"

"I expect if I marry old Robert he'll bring it up as his own. He's not so bad, as they come. Then nobody need know, and we can move on somewhere else where you can finish your school."

Margie, standing awkwardly by the kitchen table, looked across at her mother's wasted figure in the faded dressing-gown and felt a flood of tenderness and relief such as she had never experienced. At last, someone was offering a real, positive suggestion. She was going to be all right.

"Oh, mum," she said. "Would you?"

LADY SUMMERSKILL (Lab.) said the House was discussing the plight of girls who would be schoolgirls when the leaving age was raised to sixteen. The question was whether the House should give girls under sixteen—some of them aged thirteen, fourteen or fifteen—the right of abortion.

She could not agree that there was no stigma. The big centres of population (she said) are full of these girls trying to hide themselves.

If a fifteen-year-old girl in an expensive boarding school is impregnated by some lout hanging about the school . . . we all know what would happen to her. She would be whisked away and the pregnancy terminated in a discreet nursing home.

The EARL OF IDDESLEIGH (Ind.) said that in country villages when a girl became pregnant, the girl's mother brought up the child and told the village that it was hers. The villagers were not in the least deceived, but being sensible people accepted the situation.

VISCOUNT DILHORNE (C.) said he was sorry Lady Summerskill had brought such a note to the proceedings, and that Lord Silkin had made personal references.

I have two unmarried daughters (he said), one under the age of sixteen. He posed the question whether if she became pregnant I would move Heaven and earth to see that she secured an abortion somehow. I would say this to him: if she did become pregnant, I would regard it as a tragedy. If that tragedy occurred, I would certainly want to see that she had the best possible advice and help, and that does not necessarily mean abortion.

THE TIMES, *1 March 1966*

To the outward eye, then, the countryside seems sleepier than it is. True, there are birds by the million asleep in the trees; caged budgies (by the billion, it seems) cocking their pretty heads on one side in unsuspecting sleep. Express trains are howling and shrieking their way through the night.

But all this is an illusion. The fibres are not really all softened in sleep. The sinews are still ready to stiffen at command. There is plenty of life about, where it exists.

But Henry M...... lies as dead as before, beside his bicycle and poor Mrs S...... sleeps on with the memory of his love-making still warm in her mind, not knowing that it has been hers for the last time.

Detective-Sergeant Hubert L......, on the other hand, is ruefully awake; and on his way to a flat where a nervous, sleepless woman has heard "noises" coming from the flat above. Where he will soon discover Mr C......'s body, victim of another sort of twisted love (or its shadow) in the shape of Arthur.

Clive L......, he is sleeping fitfully at home, his wife soundly at a nearby hotel where the proprietor is an old friend. The *au-pair* has cried herself to sleep. The two gentlemen poker-players have disappeared into the night which, for them, is monotonously represented by solid, double-fronted suburban houses built with partial central heating.

Poor prostitute Queenie, the semi-pro who made such a bad mistake when she chose a man with bottles of whisky and gin, is in Casualty at the hospital, all stitched and bound and white-faced. She has been put on one side, on a stretcher, while a bed is found for her in the overcrowded hospital. The man who biffed her is knocking up the woman he calls his "wife," though they have never been married; kicking up hell, until she finally lets him in to sleep, drunk in his clothes, on the downstairs sofa the rest of the night.

The young ladies at the "hen-house" are in various states of nocturnal composure. Clarissa in curlers and a hair net. Georgina with traces of depilatory wax on her upper lip. Millie with her snub nose still stuck in the book she has fallen asleep reading.

Fiona curled up like a squirrel, dreaming of her mother's death in a hunting accident.

Drusilla and Caroline both fast asleep in one of the beds in the room they share together. And Gwenda whispering to the young, naked man beside her to be quiet, for God's sake, and not to breathe so loudly, as her room is directly under Captain T......'s.

Chapter 23

2 a.m.

SEXCRIME

And all the little emptiness of love.
Rupert Brook, "Peace"

The night sleeper rattled and roared towards Edinburgh with
most of the passengers tucked up asleep. But Mavis S...... had
only just got on. Her two suitcases, in powder blue padded
matching leather, stood now in the corridor of a sleeping-coach.
Directing herself towards a pool of light, she found an attendant
dozing, shirt-sleeved, in his cabin and roused him.

"Excuse me." Then, louder. "Excuse me—I've got a bed booked
on this train."

The man woke up, twitching his head. He was young, only
about thirty-two. He had dark, thick, wavy hair and the same
jet-coloured eyes. At first she thought he was coloured, then she
saw that his skin was naturally sallow. Probably Spanish stock
she thought.

"Yes, miss." He yawned, covering his thick lips with the back
of one hand, and smiled. "Don't get much chance for a kip on
this trip," he said. "Now, let's see. Your name, please?"

She told him, leaning halfway into the cabin where an electric fire was burning on the floor. She looked again at it and saw it was a cooking ring, with a steaming kettle standing beside it. He followed the direction of her glance.

"Good thing you nudged me," he said. "I was making myself a cup of tea. Like one?"

"Thanks." She was surprised but not ungrateful. It had been a long wait for the train, the only one which would get her back to the Infirmary in time for her ward duty tomorrow. She could do with a 'cuppa'.

"Then I'll get you fixed up afterwards," he said. "Plenty of room on the train tonight. There's nothing to worry about." He looked at her appreciatively. "You won't need much beauty sleep, any old how," he said familiarly.

Her smile betrayed the first hint of her unease. *Should she be doing this?* She looked down the corridor and saw the departing back of a woman in a dressing gown. The glimpse of domestic respectability gave her confidence.

She accepted his invitation to sit on the ordinary, rexine-covered seat along one side of the cabin. "Is this where you sleep?" she asked. He laughed. "When I get time," he said. Then she took the scalding tea from him and enjoyed stirring it to melt the generous helping of sugar he had given her. "That'll make you feel better," he said. "More like facing a night aboard one of these old rattlers."

From the way he spoke, she placed him as West Country. Cornish, perhaps. She had spent a holiday in Cornwall, with her mother and father, when they were alive, in a small car; staying at bed-and-breakfast houses round the coast. Her memory was of cream-teas, sandy beaches and an earth closet.

She noticed him pull the door to, but thought he did so only to prevent it banging, now that she was no longer leaning against it. All at once he was on the seat beside her, looking keenly at her through his dusky-ebony eyes. His gaze seemed to extend an invitation which frightened her. She sipped her tea in too much haste and burnt the inside of her mouth.

"Like some more milk?" he asked solicitously. Then: "My, you're a pretty one!"

She raised her eyes and tried to look forbiddingly serious and aloof. "Nonsense," she said. "But thank you. Now I must be going, if you don't mind." She put the cup down on the shelf-like table, still half-full and steaming.

"You haven't finished your tea yet," he pointed out.

"I must get to bed. I'm really very tired."

He just looked at her, the same quizzical expression buried deep behind the smouldering charcoal of his eyes. Then she felt him move towards her, stealthily, like a cat. His arm snaked out and slithered across her shoulder, her back. She was being drawn towards him, suddenly unable to resist the sheer magnetic pull of this male animal with his mesmeric glance.

She only just managed to avoid his kiss. His lips came down like the beak of a preying bird and she swung her head wildly. At first he seemed to enjoy her resistance. As she struggled, swinging her head to avoid his mouth, he laughed. She smelt beer on his breath and was frightened. Finally, he forced her head still with his own and ravished her lips.

For a while he seemed content to kiss her. Then his hand found the front of her blouse and the crisp top of the bra cup underneath it. His fingers began wrenching and twisting at the fabric.

She gave a gasp of shock and anger, afraid that he would damage her clothing. She tried hard, this time, to wrench herself free. He pushed her backwards and she fell onto the seat. His arms pinioned her.

She did not scream, because she did not want his hands on her mouth, on her neck, throttling her. She saw his figure above her, blurred in the half light, and kicked out at it, feeling her toe connect, and hearing his grunt of pain and fury. Then he was on top of her, trying to force her with all his might.

The ugly wrestle continued for about ten minutes before he pulled himself together. Then he let her go and sat down. "I'm sorry, missy," he said. "But it was only a bit of fun. You're all right, are you?"

She said nothing. She was bruised and shaking and wonderfully thankful he had left her alone at last. Now, all she wanted was to get away from this horrible man, and into her own bed. "You'd better show me where my bed is," she said. "And if that's how you behave to all the girls who travel on this line at night, something ought to be done about it. It's disgusting!"

He took her ticket and held open the door politely. "No offence," he said. "I said you were a pretty one, didn't I?"

She smiled in spite of herself. "Oh, get on," she said. "Some of you men ought to be sterilized, you really should!"

No woman really believes that any man is as big a skunk as he acts, and it is, therefore, pitifully easy for a man to take a woman in.

Margorie Proops, DAILY MIRROR, *29 March 1966*

In Beckenham, the wife-swapping party was getting into its stride, more correctly its second wind. Three couples had spent the late evening, until shortly before midnight, respectably in each others' company: Bob and Jill, Harry and Joan; and our old friends (the Proust fans) Conrad and Marcia. The drinks had been purposely made a little stronger than usual; otherwise it might have been any suburban social gathering. In fact, this sextet had been brought together by the correspondence columns of the *Golden Band*, a magazine circulated privately (by subscriptions only) among married couples.

Bob and Jill, whose house this party was in, had been the original advertisers. They had put "broad-minded" and "unconventional" in their advertisement, for "married couples interested in mutual entertainment", leaving an exciting doubt as to the prospects in store for the answerers. Harry and Joan had been rather tickled by the idea; they had been married three years. They had replied to the advertisement and later met the other couple, as suggested, for a mutual "sizing-up". This had been in London, in a Soho restaurant.

It had turned out that they both shared the same notion of what "broad-mindedness" and "unconventionality" should mean. Before long, the first couple had invited their new friends to their home for "a try-out".

It had been a huge success. Neither of the two wives (who, apart from their colouring, might almost have been sisters—they were so alike in gesture and carriage and build) seemed to feel the least embarrassment at taking off her clothes in front of the other. The men, more boisterously, followed their lead. The interchange of partners was effected with glowing enthusiasm by all parties.

Afterwards—on this initial occasion there had only been the one, brief and indeed (when compared with later activities) modest and circumspect bout of activity—the two women had disappeared upstairs to re-robe, leaving the men to restore their energies with strong whiskies and soda-water.

Then Harry had suggested his old college pal, Conrad. Bit of an "odd-ball" in some ways, but definitely not a square. He and that gorgeous C.N.D. girl he'd married, Marcia, would be just the job for one of these shows. The suggestion had been made to Bob and Jill and they had heartily approved the extension of the circle.

Tonight the couples had met, by appointment, at half-past nine. Conrad and Marcia had turned up a shade late and there had been a lot of teasing until Conrad had allowed himself to be persuaded to tell the story of his "education" of the young baby-sitter. When he stated the facts, including the girl's curious passion during the culmination of the proceedings, and his own increasing inability to keep a strictly academic view of the matter, there were great shock waves of laughter and a good deal of touching of hands and bodies among the couples. At 11.35—twenty-five minutes earlier than usual, and after listening carefully at the foot of the stairs for sounds of their three children—Bob turned the key to lock the lounge door, and the fun began.

Tonight was no different from any of the others. They met as a rule once a week, usually on Friday or Saturday evening. There had been only one growing tendency, and that was an increasing enjoyment of *group* activities. It was during the height of one of these that, at a quarter to three, the telephone rang and went on ringing.

In somewhat the same way, the Party member knew what constituted right conduct, and in exceedingly vague, generalized terms he knew what kinds of departure from it were possible. His sexual life, for example, was entirely regulated by the two Newspeak words *sexcrime* (sexual immorality) and *goodsex* (chastity). *Sexcrime* covered all sexual misdeeds whatever. It covered fornication, adultery, homosexuality, and other perversions, and, in addition, normal intercourse practised for its own sake. There was no need to enumerate them separately, since they were all equally culpable, and, in principle, all punishable by death.

In the C vocabulary, which consisted of scientific and technical words, it might be necessary to give specialized names to certain sexual aberrations, but the ordinary citizen had no need of them. He knew what was meant by *goodsex*—that is to say, normal intercourse between man and wife, for the sole purpose of begetting children, and without physical pleasure on the part of the woman: all else was *sexcrime*.

George Orwell, "Nineteen Eighty-Four" (Secker & Warburg)

Chapter 24

3 a.m.

US

In New York—five hours astern—the city is a cluster of jewelled lights and movement, while California is only now sitting out to its barbecues. Eyes are twinkling, teeth flashing; and smiles, fingers and even toes flirting. Yet London, indeed the whole of Britain, asks to be excused. The British lover has had his, and her day. Love has moved around the clock. We must wrap ourselves in dreams and depart.

Before we do, there is time for one final glance at the characters we have assembled—representing as they do true cases of our curious, though never faint-hearted, mating habits and pastimes; and for any conclusion we may feel called upon to offer in verdict on the *homo britannicus* as lover, seducer and swain.

Would you say immediately that violence and sexual licence have been more closely linked in these pages than anyone would expect? Well, blame the record. It is at fault, if anything is.

Of course millions of sweet, simple lovers' tales go unrecorded, and so cannot filter into a book like this, any more than honesty and other virtues can dominate the report of criminal courts.

So this is necessarily a nasty picture. Yet the nice—if you care to look—underlies its statistics, existing by contrast. What's that you say, madam? *No English gentleman could behave like that!* If you enjoy such precious thoughts you really should spend a week at the old Bailey (whether or not you may have to compete for your seat at the juicier trials with sixteen-and seventeen-year-old Grammar School girls and their progressive mistresses). You should also observe the quality of the British nature in the raw; in the sordid depths of which passion and God-knows-what compulsions and perversions flow like subterranean torrents.

Whatever I have managed to say, hint, imply or explain in this book is not, believe me, a gnat's whisker to the great bushy beard of our islands' baser morals in full fling.

So I make no apologies for the unseemly conduct expressed here. It is common enough. It is also, I think, international, except where our quaint predilection for the uncomfortable and the outrageously macabre go hand in hand.

Of love? Have no qualms, your Briton is tender as the next man; truer than most; and *great shakes* as a lover if legend (though offered only sub rosa) is to be even half-believed. True he does have a smudgy grey area which might be called his "court-man-ship", being a fellow who sees no point in buying a fool's paradise via cupboard-love.

But his present-giving, when it occurs at all, usually is more sincere and practical (say a nice little sewing-machine, so the little woman can darn his shirts!) than that of swains abroad. And mean? Not at all. He will share his last crisp from the bag with you—when at long last he gets to it.

In the *lingo* of love—those honeyed phrases so biologically necessary to most European males—it is true to say that he does falter badly. This is because he lacks the finesse of speech which men of action possess almost inevitably. Above all, he finds it hard to lie, and downright impossible to reveal his true, private thoughts. But, as Leonardo said, the truth is never where men shout, very seldom where they speak at all. An English lover's heart is true.

His woman, be she wife, mate, sweetheart or "just good friend", deserves him. Because she also knows a thing or two about this business of loving. For instance, that a woman who keeps herself *eternally* young is often more attractive to committees in search of voluntary recruits for tedious jobs than to her husband. She has sense enough, in most cases, to recognize the fact that he does not *want* to see her spend his money on a lot of trash which only makes her look, in his carefully guarded, secret opinion, like an old bag fitted with a brash new clasp.

That's not always the case. Sometimes (quite often, perhaps), she goes too far, and lets herself lose him. She digs in her toes and decides she's not going to be wife *and* mother. Why should she try to please him? What does he ever do for her? Selfish brute. There must be several hundreds of thousands of British women who suffocate their love in this way, when they might have built it—and the object of it—into something they would not have believed remotely possible.

But he isn't blameless here, either. Starting with school or young family life he seems determined not to permit the first hint of petticoat encroachment on his domain. His sisters, girl friends, finally his wife and most probably any daughters they may have are all subjugated to what, in his atavistically bigoted opinion, is their proper station. They can get along absolutely swimmingly with him and enjoy his comfort, love and protection, provided . . . They only have to step out of line just once to know where that "provided" starts and ends.

But before the rot sets in he's a jolly good chap and, as a lover, full of good clean healthy fun, a fine sporting outlook (nice long walks as a substitute for seeing that matinée his girl was dying for, most probably). He's a man's man, whatever that means; which probably is to say that he is exactly what women like, however much they pretend to be forced to screaming pitch by his little-boy habits (bits of motorcars in his pockets and hankies covered with tobacco juice and tar), his pathetic repertoire of breezy sayings (destined to make all her friends curl up) and the way he lets her down, flat, at parties, refusing to talk to her and being either drunk and insulting to his host or madly flirting with his hostess in the bedroom. She probably wouldn't have him any other way.

When it comes to a close focus study, as this has been, then some of the odder mutations are bound to show up. But try to see the species as a whole: there isn't any "Mister" or "Missus Average", but at least we can throw a yardstick over a few representative backs and see what it reads.

Down there in the suburban depths of Beckenham, for instance: what is the merit value of our wife-exchangers? They don't, on the surface anyway, seem to rate as anything but cheap erotic thrill-seekers of a particularly nasty pattern, likely—indeed almost certain—to end up badly and perhaps tragically. Is this their score? I think it is. I also think it is a sign of the times, of the restless impotence of the Age of the Bomb and other inevitabilities, that they exist at all. But they are in our midst to a somewhat alarming degree; no worse here than elsewhere in Europe (and perhaps less *per capita* than in post-Kinsey suburban U.S.A.). But definitely here.

Detective-Sergeant L......—is he a biased and uncharitable myth, intended to sling even more mud at a long-suffering police force which does its unarmed best to suppress a growing anti-society, so that the rest of us can enjoy at least some of our earnings? He is certainly not intended to be typical, or even in his case representative. L...... belongs to an imperfect corps in an imperfect country in an imperfect world. He is the perfect imperfection. Dislike and distrust him as much as you care to, but do not altogether disbelieve in him. His colleagues know there is a bad apple in every bushel; that is why they keep detectives in the Force whose duty sometimes is to watch other detectives.

Arthur and Mr C......? A very ordinary, common case. Rather sad, and offered without comment in view of the great hah-hah going on recently about the rights of consenting males in private. But certainly a sizable sector of the whole sex problem. One day, perhaps, the answer will be found; biologically as well as psychologically, to adjust and attune the chromosome and genetic patterns of man, like changing the key of a musical, stringed instrument. Until then, there will always be such tragedies. Many worse.

Dr Julian de S...... and his wife are more unusual, perhaps. Their marriage seems blighted. Perhaps it is. Their case follows a typical case history (is, indeed, drawn from an actual happening). How it can hope to resolve itself is not for us here. But the very British situation of foreigners living in our midst (as *us*, with *our* passports, habits and customs), then developing their own curiously alien mannerisms, is a part of the whole. It is what makes areas of Britain essentially cosmopolitan.

In Clive L......, of course, there is much more of the immature cad than the real heel; what Victorians would have called "a loose fish". He stands a very good chance of making everything up with his spirited wife. Her caprice could not have happened a few years ago, because morals at that level have slid a long way downwards. But it is exactly plausible today. And, as a ploy, she may well have taken the winning trick.

Captain T...... is, I suppose, an unredeemably nasty piece-of-work; yet I feel sympathy for him (more than the law would feel, no doubt). His loneliness and "outsiderness" in a world of Beatles and boutiques is slightly touching. The girls are silly and lecherous, when it suits them. He is just a harmlessly disgusting old man.

But my main sympathy—perhaps you guessed—is for Fred F....... Fred, it seems to me, made the fatal mistake of being a "doer" rather than a "viewer". In this electronic world, we are all prone to persuasion to watch, rather than to take part. He broke through these enticements and went into action.

It is to me only additionally poignant that, like the silly clot he is, he immediately plonked both feet in it; landing himself in the sort of trouble which will never leave him for the rest of his days on British soil, and probably elsewhere. But what can you do about such men? Fred, if he had been just a non-conformist, with a bit of brain, would have been safe as houses; he might even have been made mayor. As the *anti*-conformist he is he dosen't stand a pickpocket's chance in a nudist colony. Better shake our heads and pass on; it is pointless worrying about poor Fred.

The Duke of S...... is a bit of a card, don't you think? Of course, experience shows that the Duchess is just as likely to pop back into his arms as into any others, when once she has done with her current spate of lovers, and is not physically in the Bahamas. Nothing, with these exotic people, ever seems quite real. They *are* sad, angry and hurt, of course; all these things. But I think he really only pinched her diary so that he could read it to his cronies at the club. If it is true, as was said, that she expressed opinions about them in it, he would be assured of an audience.

We have to leave, now, but not before we blow a kiss to the girls at the high-class call-girl place round the back of Marble Arch. Do you find it hard to believe such places exist? A leading detective told me he once found one where "madam" was the mother of a famous motor-racing driver. She preferred looking after these odd, funny "benties". I don't mean to laugh at them; they are probably very tragic. But how can you keep a straight face when you hear of a man paying a girl to appear naked at the other end of his long sitting room, so that he can pelt her with cream-buns?

The couple in Notting Hill who have to live together are another true-as-gospel contemporary situation. It is still, even in this day and age, fantastically difficult to overcome prejudice about monogamy in Britain.

Of course, I suppose you guessed that the milk roundsman was the murderer of that wretched little pregnant girl in the North?

He didn't take long to confess, because somehow it always seems possible to these horribly twisted misfits that somebody in authority will understand their problems. Nobody does. But, nowadays, they keep them alive; and hoping; instead of relieving them, and us, of the burden of their demented and dangerous existence.

I should like to say, as the clock's minute hand slides up towards the top, to make four o'clock one more, "this is where we came in . . .". But it is not quite so, is it? After all, no lover lives the same day twice. So be it.

Beware Au Pair

by Liselotte Durand

'Au Pair wanted for happy English home in the country, own room, daily kept, one day a week free time. Write Box Q.1237, The Times, E.C.4.'

This was the innocent-looking advertisement which brought young naïve Swiss girl Liselotte Durand to Britain. But she soon found out that life in England was far from conventional.

She met some very odd people, such as the crusty, bicycle-riding Major; Mr. Dorman-Jones, who enjoyed his own corny jokes if no-one else did; and Kate Carter, who wrote excellent advice on organisation for a woman's paper, but kept her own home in disorganised chaos!

She worked for two eccentric and picturesque bachelors in Chelsea and was later employed to care for a neurotic poodle who hated to be left alone. Liselotte also caught a glimpse of the wild teenage scene, where drug parties and sex orgies seemed to be commonplace.

FOUR ■ SQUARE EDITION 3s. 6d.

How to Make Love in Five Languages

by Doris Lilly

Powder Madison. All American and all girl.

Disenchanted with the men in the United States. Off to Europe to find out whether European men are as tiresome as the men she knows in New York.

In Italy she found ...

Amore (an Italian may even marry you. If he does, he will be unfaithful but seldom jealous since he is quite sure he is the world's best lover).

In Spain she found ...

Amor (the Spaniard is isolated, arrogant, suspicious, wary and independent to a fierce fault).

In Germany she found ...

Liebe (a German will walk across Europe in his bare feet, swim in the ice and die with his boots on. But he will not cross the street against the light).

In France she found ...

Amour (a Frenchman likes to think of himself as an intellectual lover, but that does not mean that he wants to sit around discussing existentialism until dawn).

In England she found ...

Love (the Englishman does not love women. He loves beer, dogs, and football. Women he has as chums).

And who knows—maybe she is right. Anyway, her book is a fascinating study of sex and seduction from Sweden to Sicily.

Every girl should read it. So should every man.

FOUR 4 SQUARE EDITION 5s. 0d.